Skills Practice Book 2

Themes 4 5 6

voices reading

grade **3**

Illustrations by Joe Boddy

ISBN-13: 978-0-7367-4821-6
ISBN-10: 0-7367-4821-0

Zaner-Bloser, Inc., P.O. Box 16764, Columbus, Ohio 43216-6764
1-800-421-3018, www.zaner-bloser.com

Printed in the United States of America

06 07 08 09 10 (4495) 5 4 3 2 1

Table of Contents

Theme 4

Theme 5

Table of Contents (continued)

Theme 6

Name _____

Sequence Think about the story **Jim Thorpe's Bright Path**. Complete the timeline with events from Jim's life from the box.

goes to Haskell Institute

twin brother, Charlie, dies

goes to boarding school

mother dies

learns to ride a horse

goes to Carlisle Indian School

Event

Age   3   6   9   11   14   16

Name _____

Short oo Sound (look) Write the word from the box that best completes each sentence.

good	wooden	hood	stood	book
cook	soot	hook	foot	shook

1. I am always excited about reading a new _____.

2. My grandmother will _____ tacos for dinner tonight.

3. I _____ on a stool to reach the sink.

4. Uncle Pete had _____ all over his clothes after he cleaned the fireplace.

5. I hang my jacket on a _____.

6. My cousin _____ the gift to figure out what was inside.

7. The _____ chest was filled with wool sweaters.

8. The mechanic checked under the _____ of the red car.

9. A four-leaf clover is said to bring _____ luck.

10. Kai broke his right _____ because he fell off the bed.

voicesreading Grade 3

Name _____

Write a vocabulary word on each line to replace the words in **dark print**.

> resented   insults   clothe   drafty   tanks   relay

1. His **disrespectful remarks** hurt my feelings. _____

2. The rickety, old barn is **allowing wind to get inside**. _____

3. The army sometimes uses **large, protected vehicles with guns**. _____

4. She **felt angered by** his lack of concern about her lost puppy. _____

5. My teacher asked me **to pass on** the homework assignment to my sister. _____

6. Parents **provide something to wear** and feed their children. _____

Name _____

Choosing and Ordering Important Information Look at the timeline about Rosa Parks. Use some of the information to write a short paragraph.

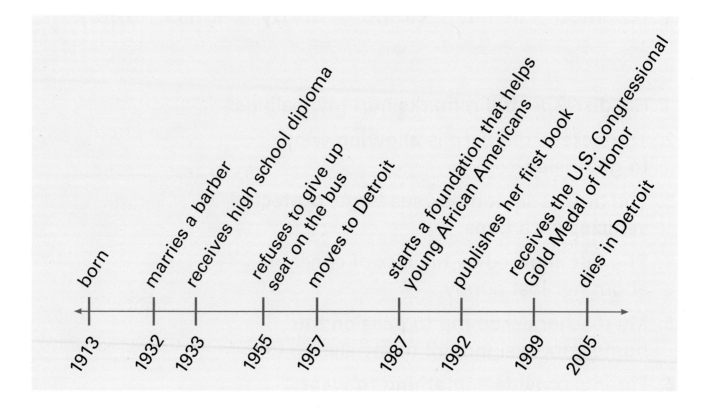

_____

_____

_____

_____

_____

voicesreading Grade 3

Copyright © Zaner-Bloser, Inc.

Name _____

r-Controlled er, ir, ur Shade the bubble next to the word that is spelled correctly and best completes each sentence.

I. The waiter will _____ dessert after everyone finishes their dinner.

   ○ **surve**   ○ **serve**   ○ **sirve**   ○ **searve**

2. Aunt Lisa always carries extra change and tissues in her _____.

   ○ **purse**   ○ **perse**   ○ **pirse**   ○ **pierce**

3. The _____ at the grocery store gave my sister free stickers.

   ○ **clurk**   ○ **clirk**   ○ **klerk**   ○ **clerk**

4. The infielder tagged another player before he slid into _____ base.

   ○ **therd**   ○ **thurd**   ○ **third**   ○ **theard**

5. A little red _____ was sitting on the ledge outside my bedroom window.

   ○ **bird**   ○ **berd**   ○ **burd**   ○ **beard**

6. The kind _____ offered me ice cream after the doctor removed my tonsils.

   ○ **nerse**   ○ **nurse**   ○ **nirse**   ○ **nurce**

7. I spoke in a very _____ voice when I told Tony to stop teasing my brother.

   ○ **sturn**   ○ **stirn**   ○ **stern**   ○ **steern**

8. We read a story about how pioneers used to _____ butter.

   ○ **chern**   ○ **chirn**   ○ **chuurn**   ○ **churn**

Name _____

Spelling Words

brook	crooked	foot	footsteps	good-bye	goods
hoof	hook	nook	shook	soot	wood

voicesreading Grade 3

Copyright © Zaner-Bloser, Inc.

Write the spelling word that belongs in each group.

I. stream, creek, _____

2. fishing pole, line, _____

3. fireplace, wood, _____

4. curved, bent, _____

Write the spelling word that completes each analogy.

5. **Finger** is to **hand** as **toe** is to _____.

6. **Dog** is to **paw** as **horse** is to _____.

7. **Library** is to **books** as **store** is to _____.

8. **Arriving** is to **hello** as **leaving** is to _____.

Unscramble the letters in **dark print** to make a spelling word.

9. **knoo**   _____   10. **dwoo**   _____

II. **oskoh**   _____   12. **tepsofots**   _____

Name _____

Using a Timeline Using a **timeline** can help you organize information before you begin writing.

Example: **Studying for a Test**

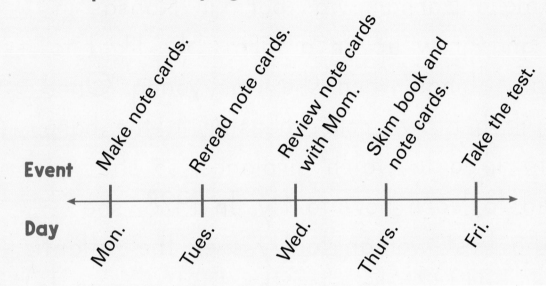

Think about something you accomplished this week (learned a new song, completed a puzzle, etc.). Make a timeline that shows how you accomplished this task.

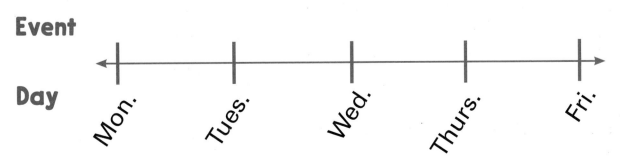

Name _____

Biography Read this example of a biography.

Amelia Earhart was born in Kansas in 1897, and grew up on a farm. She liked to do many things when she was young. Once, she built her own roller coaster in the barn!

She liked to watch airplanes, so she decided to learn how to fly. In 1928, she was the first woman to fly over the Atlantic Ocean. In 1932, she was the first woman to fly by herself across the Atlantic Ocean. In 1935, she became the first person to fly from Hawaii to California. Her last flight was in 1937. After flying 20,000 miles over the Pacific Ocean, she disappeared. Her disappearance is still a mystery.

voicesreading Grade 3

Copyright © Zaner-Bloser, Inc.

Name _____

Analogies Write a word from the box to complete each analogy.

short	sad	house	fish	bed	tear
shape	jungle	fruit	store	cat	trees

1. **Laugh** is to **happy** as **cry** is to _____.

2. **Cow** is to **farm** as **monkey** is to _____.

3. **Bird** is to **nest** as **person** is to _____.

4. **Puppy** is to **dog** as **kitten** is to _____.

5. **Carrot** is to **vegetable** as **apple** is to _____.

6. **Grass** is to **ground** as **leaves** are to _____.

7. **Big** is to **little** as **tall** is to _____.

8. **Book** is to **library** as **food** is to _____.

9. **Plate** is to **table** as **pillow** is to _____.

10. **Fur** is to **animals** as **scales** are to _____.

11. **Glass** is to **break** as **paper** is to _____.

12. **Green** is to **color** as **triangle** is to _____.

Name _____

Complete the crossword puzzle using the vocabulary words from the box.

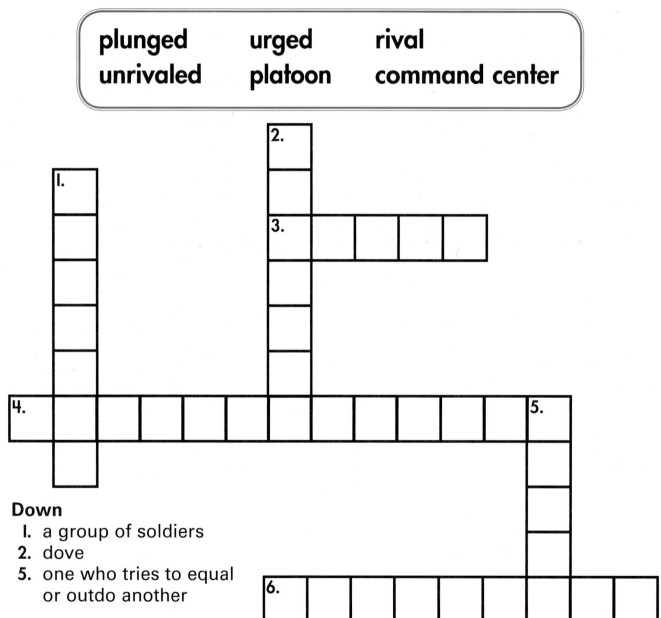

plunged   urged   rival
unrivaled   platoon   command center

Down
1. a group of soldiers
2. dove
5. one who tries to equal or outdo another

Across
3. suggested strongly
4. the military's main office during a war
6. having no equal

voicesreading Grade 3

Name _____

Sequence Use the timeline on page 5 to write a paragraph about Jim Thorpe. Use time-order words to tell when the events happened.

_____

_____

_____

_____

_____

_____

_____

_____

_____

_____

_____

_____

Name _____

Choosing Subject and Object Pronouns Write the pronoun that best completes each sentence on the line.

1. _____ will study for the test for at least one hour.
   (**I, Me**)

2. The cats were so scared, _____ ran up a tree.
   (**them, they**)

3. I asked Trent if _____ would like to join our soccer team.
   (**he, him**)

4. _____ are going with us on vacation this summer.
   (**They, Them**)

5. The teacher gave _____ new books to read in class.
   (**us, we**)

6. _____ mom offered to drive us to the theater.
   (**She, Her**)

7. _____ are going to invite our new neighbors to a picnic.
   (**We, Us**)

8. Two of my friends ride the bus to school with _____.
   (**me, I**)

9. My brother likes it when I sing to _____.
   (**him, he**)

10. I will ask _____ if she will join us for lunch tomorrow.
    (**she, her**)

Name _____

Timeline You can use a Timeline to organize events for your biography.

Character Development Practice

Week 1, Day 4
Partner Sharing

Name _____

What Is My Bright Path? As you learned in the story **Jim Thorpe's Bright Path,** Jim Thorpe loved to run and play sports. What do you love to do? What values will guide you? As you think about the things you like to do, answer the questions below. Then share your answers with your partner.

I. The things I love to do are _____

_____

_____

_____ .

2. The values that will guide me on my path are _____

_____

_____

_____

_____ .

Name _____

Short oo Sound (look) Read the words in each tic-tac-toe board. Draw a line through the three words in each board that have the **short oo** sound, as in **look**.

I.

cool	good	shook
soot	book	goose
moon	foot	coop

2.

hood	zoo	food
zoom	nook	tool
soon	boot	soot

3.

goose	too	wood
snooze	crook	shoot
took	roof	tooth

4.

stood	hook	foot
hood	wood	loose
spoon	stool	moon

Name _____

Spelling Words

brook	crooked	foot	footsteps	good-bye	goods
hoof	hook	nook	shook	soot	wood

voicesreading Grade 3

Replace the words in **dark print** with a spelling word from the box.

I. The sign was **bent** after a car hit it. _____

2. We buy **items** when we shop. _____

3. I like to read in a **little cozy space**. _____

4. A blacksmith put the horseshoe on the horse's **foot**. _____

5. When camp was over, we said **farewell**. _____

6. I hear **the sound of feet** coming! _____

7. A **stream** flows through our yard. _____

8. The ground **trembled** for a long time after the earthquake was over. _____

9. I hang my robe on a **metal hanger**. _____

10. The deck is made of **fallen timber**. _____

11. Our fireplace is covered with **black residue**. _____

12. I've grown a whole **twelve inches**. _____

Copyright © Zaner-Bloser, Inc.

Name _____

Dividing VCCV Words Rewrite the words in **dark print** on the lines. Draw a line between the syllables.

1. **pencil** _____

2. **center** _____

3. **cannot** _____

4. **sister** _____

5. **thunder** _____

6. **happen** _____

7. **holly** _____

8. **turkey** _____

9. **kitten** _____

10. **messy** _____

11. **mitten** _____

12. **dinner** _____

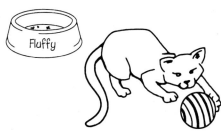

Name _____

Use this checklist when you revise your biography.

Revising Checklist: Narrative

yes	**no**	Does the biography use interesting words and phrases to tell about someone?
yes	**no**	Does the biography include important dates and events in the person's life?
yes	**no**	Does each paragraph include interesting facts and information about the person?
yes	**no**	Does the biography include several reasons why the person is important to you?
yes	**no**	Do time-order words tell when events happened?
yes	**no**	Are subject and object pronouns used correctly?

voicesreading Grade 3

Name _____

resented   insults   clothe   drafty   tanks   relay

Write the vocabulary word from the box that matches each definition.

I. to provide with something to wear _____

2. to pass on _____

3. allowing wind inside _____

4. large, protected vehicles _____

5. felt angered by _____

6. mean remarks _____

Write the vocabulary word that belongs in each group.

7. enraged, angered, _____

8. ships, airplanes, _____

9. pass on, tell, _____

10. breezy, windy, _____

II. disrespectful, attacks, _____

12. dress, cover, _____

Name _____

Choose a vocabulary word from the box to complete each sentence.

voicesreading Grade 3

plunged	urged	rival
unrivaled	platoon	command center

I. This black bean soup is _____ by any soup I have ever tasted.

2. An army _____ can be many miles from a battlefield.

3. The _____ lived in tents on the hot, desert sand.

4. The teacher _____ all of his students to study for the test.

5. The rabbit _____ into the bush before the fox could catch him.

6. My tennis _____ won the match because he played better.

Copyright © Zaner-Bloser, Inc.

Name _____

Evaluate Think about the characters in **Jim Thorpe's Bright Path**. What would each character say in the following situations?

I. What would Jim's father say if Jim said he didn't like school?

_____

_____

2. What would Jim say if somebody told him he couldn't do something, like play football?

_____

_____

3. What would Jim say if someone said Native Americans cannot do what other people do?

_____

_____

4. What would Jim's father have said if he had lived to see what his son had accomplished?

_____

_____

Name _____

Fact and Opinion Read the statements about the story **America's Champion Swimmer: Gertrude Ederle**. Complete the chart by putting a ✔ in the correct column.

Statement	Fact	Opinion
I. Trudy swam better than any of the other swimmers.		
2. At fifteen, Trudy won her first big race.		
3 Trudy was "just a plain home girl."		
4. Trudy won three medals at the Olympics in Paris.		
5. Many people were sure Trudy wouldn't do well.		
6. Gee, but it's cold.		
7. Trudy wore a red bathing cap.		
8. The waves in the ocean were twenty feet high.		
9. It was eerie being in the water all alone.		
10. All the women of the world will celebrate Gertrude's success.		

voicesreading Grade 3

Copyright © Zaner-Bloser, Inc.

Name _____

r-Controlled ar, or Think of the word each picture stands for. Read the sentence and circle the word that has the same vowel sound.

1.  The farmer had just finished his chores when he saw the sheep wander away.

2. 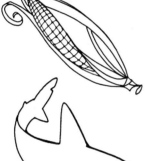 I would like to have more time to gaze at the stars.

3.  We saw starfish in the fish tank.

4.  Sometimes I get bored on long car rides.

5.  My dog barks a lot when she hears thunder.

6.  I will mark the row where you should plant the corn.

Name _____

Draw a line from each vocabulary word in **dark print** to its definition.

l. **conquer**   a group of people who like to participate in the same activity

2. **stress**

                                                  very active and forceful

3. **guts**   acted as if something or someone is worthless or bad

4. **aggressive**

                                                  to overcome something that is difficult

5. **sneered**

                                                  a state of worry

6. **club**   courage

voicesreading Grade 3

Name _____

Paraphrasing Good writers take information and put it into their own words.

> **Example:** The most important single ingredient in the formula of success is knowing how to get along with people.   —Theodore Roosevelt
>
> To be successful, you must get along with people. **(Paraphrasing)**

Paraphrase each quotation. Write your answers on the lines.

1. It isn't enough to talk about peace. One must believe in it. And it isn't enough to believe in it. One must work at it.
                                                    —Eleanor Roosevelt

_____

_____

2. In order to succeed, your desire for success should be greater than your fear of failure.   —Bill Cosby

_____

_____

3. Do not go where the path may lead, go instead where there is no path, and leave a trail.   —Ralph Waldo Emerson

_____

_____

Name _____

Short oo Sound (look) Read each word in the box. If the word has a **long oo** sound, write it under **Moon**. If the word has a **short oo** sound, write it under **Book**.

voicesreading Grade 3

shoot	tooth	soot	noon
shook	stood	troop	crook
foot	bloom	spoon	brook
cook	balloon	cartoon	wood

Moon

Book

_____

_____

_____

_____

_____

_____

Copyright © Zaner-Bloser, Inc.

Name _____

Spelling Words

bar	forty	gorilla	large	morning	part
port	shore	short	snore	sort	warn

Unscramble the letters in **dark print** to spell words from the box. Write the words correctly on the lines

1. torfy _____

2. ningrom _____

3. torsh _____

4. rost _____

5. torp _____

6. geral _____

7. tarp _____

8. nores _____

9. rawn _____

10. shreo _____

11. illarog _____

12. arb _____

Name _____

Photographs and Captions Look at the photo and caption to answer the questions.

Bird Song (**Title**)
Toby Williams (**Photographer**)
Black and white film (**Materials**)
16 in. x 20 in. (**Size**)
Evans Museum of Art (**Location**)

I. Who took the photo? _____

2. What is the name of the photo? _____

3. What materials were used? _____

4. What is the size of the photo? _____

5. Where is the photo displayed? _____

Name _____

Using a Thesaurus Use a thesaurus to replace each word in **dark print** with a synonym.

1. A **pretty** bluebird flew from tree to tree. _____

2. She had a birthday party with her **friends**. _____

3. It was very **kind** of her to invite the
entire class. _____

4. Koto brought a gift with a **nice** bow
on top. _____

5. Everyone had a **good** time swinging at
the piñata. _____

Use a thesaurus to replace each word in **dark print** with an antonym.

6. The **large** dog would not stop barking at
the doorbell. _____

7. A **brave** mouse crept across the kitchen
floor. _____

8. I was very **sad** when the football game
was over. _____

9. The princess complained that the mattress
was too **hard**. _____

10. I like a **warm** glass of milk before I go
to bed. _____

Name _____

Write the vocabulary word from the box that matches each definition.

shamed	paved the way	husky
heartily	progressed	image

I. made to feel bad or guilty _____

2. having a solid body _____

3. a lasting impression _____

4. moved forward _____

5. made progress easier _____

6. with great hunger _____

Now, use the vocabulary words in complete sentences.

7. _____

8. _____

9. _____

10. _____

II. _____

12. _____

voicesreading Grade 3

Name _____

Fact and Opinion Read each statement. Write **F** if the statement is a **fact**. Write **O** if the statement is an **opinion**.

1. Swimming is the hardest sport. _____

2. The backstroke is a swimming stroke. _____

3. Everyone should learn how to swim. _____

4. It is more fun to swim in the ocean than in a pool. _____

5. Many pools have a deep end and a shallow end. _____

6. Wearing goggles allows swimmers to open their eyes under water. _____

7. Girls and boys should not swim together. _____

8. Chlorine is used to keep pool water clean. _____

9. Some beaches do not allow flotation devices in the water. _____

10. Everyone should use flotation devices. _____

11. You must have long arms and legs to be a good swimmer. _____

12. Most Olympic swimmers practice many hours every day. _____

Name _____

Pronouns Used for Things Choose a pronoun from the box to replace the words in **dark print** in each sentence.

| This | That | These | Those |

1. **The toys beside me** are the ones I play with the most. _____

2. **The toys in my neighbor's yard** belong to her grandson, Sam. _____

3. **The kitten I am holding** was adopted from the shelter. _____

4. **The animal shelter downtown** is a fun place to visit. _____

5. **The basket that is next to me** is where the kitten will sleep. _____

6. **The basket in the garage** is too far away from the house. _____

7. **The ball in my hand** is the kitten's favorite toy. _____

8. **The bone and the ball out in the yard** are the dog's toys. _____

voicesreading Grade 3

Copyright © Zaner-Bloser, Inc.

Name _____

Overcoming Discrimination What can we do to overcome discrimination in our society? Choose one example of discrimination from the web on the board. Then brainstorm with your partner ways to overcome this discrimination. Complete the sentences below.

Example of Discrimination: _____

_____

I. One way people are treated unfairly is

_____

_____

_____ .

2. Two ways our society could overcome this kind of

discrimination are _____

_____

_____

_____

_____ .

voicesreading Grade 3

Copyright © Zaner-Bloser, Inc.

Name _____

r-controlled ar, or Write the word from the box that matches each clue.

voicesreading Grade 3

spark	smart	chord	bark	former	chart
farmer	morning	born	sport	market	before

1. This is the noise a dog makes. _____

2. This rhymes with **cart**. _____

3. This means the opposite of **after**. _____

4. This means "brought into life." _____

5. A person who grows crops is this. _____

6. Football is an example of this. _____

7. This means "beginning of the day." _____

8. People can buy food here. _____

9. This is a flash of light. _____

10. This means "the one before." _____

11. This is a musical note. _____

12. This is a place to organize information. _____

Name _____

Circle the misspelled words in the paragraph and write them correctly on the lines below.

    The larg gerila sat under a tree all morening. His home was patr of the zoo near a small poret town. One day, fortee people walked the shorte distance from the shor to his home. As they came close, he let out a snort that sounded like a sorte of snor to worn the people to stay away. Then, one of the visitors gave him a candy bare. The zookeeper quickly came to remind the visitors not to feed the animals. Candy isn't good for gorillas!

I. _____   2. _____   3. _____

4. _____   5. _____   6. _____

7. _____   8. _____   9. _____

10. _____   II. _____   12. _____

voicesreading Grade 3

Name _____

Analogies Circle the word that best completes each analogy.

1. **Bird** is to **tree** as **bear** is to _____.
   cave   animal   cub

2. **Airplane** is to **sky** as **train** is to _____.
   transportation   tracks   caboose

3. **January** is to **winter** as **July** is to _____.
   beach   flower   summer

4. **Big** is to **large** as **little** is to _____.
   small   giant   size

5. **Mean** is to **kind** as **ugly** is to _____.
   nice   pretty   looks

6. **Spoon** is to **scoop** as **knife** is to _____.
   silverware   dishes   slice

7. **Pilot** is to **airport** as **doctor** is to _____.
   hospital   patient   sick

8. **Soft** is to **whisper** as **loud** is to _____.
   quiet   yell   sound

9. **Snake** is to **reptile** as **cow** is to _____.
   milk   mammal   horse

10. **Robin** is to **bird** as **poodle** is to _____.
    collie   animal   dog

voicesreading Grade 3

Name _____

Circle the vocabulary word that best completes each sentence.

I. The ducks _____ at the ugly duckling when he asked if he could play with them.

urged   **clothed**   **aggressive**   **sneered**

2. She wants to _____ her fear of high places by climbing the mountain.

conquer   **aggressive**   **relay**   **control**

3. He felt some _____ when they closed the rocket's door and started the countdown.

guts   **stress**   **rival**   **fleeing**

4. I plan to start a _____ for students who are interested in classical music.

image   **club**   **stutter**   **rumor**

5. Hungry animals can be very _____ when they are looking for food.

drafty   **husky**   **aggressive**   **refreshing**

6. It took a lot of _____ to surf on that huge wave!

guts   **rival**   **relay**   **plush**

voicesreading Grade 3

Name _____

Use the vocabulary words from the box to complete the paragraph.

shamed	paved the way	husky
heartily	progressed	image

The first person who stepped onto the moon left us with an

_____ that will last for many years. Neil Armstrong

looked _____ in the bulky spacesuit when he made

the first human footprint on the moon. That first small step

_____ for our future in space exploration. We

shouldn't feel _____ by the great things our

country has done! We have _____ much since then.

I _____ support more trips to the moon

and beyond.

Name _____

Sequence Think about the story **America's Champion Swimmer: Gertrude Ederle**. Read the list of events from the story. Number the events from **1** to **6** in the order they happened.

_____ Gertrude successfully swims across the English Channel.

_____ Gertrude wins 3 medals at the Olympics in Paris.

_____ Gertrude joins the New York Swimming Association.

_____ Gertrude tries to swim across the English Channel, but fails.

_____ Gertrude learns to swim.

_____ Gertrude swims 17 miles from lower Manhattan to Sandy Hook, New Jersey.

Now, complete the timeline below with the events from above.

Event

Name _____

Categorize and Classify Think about the story **My Name Is Celia**. Complete the graphic organizer with information from the story.

Music

Celia

Places She Lived

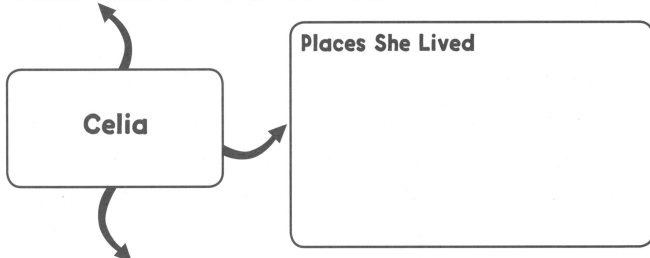

Obstacles

Name _____

The u_e Pattern Look at the pictures. Circle the word that names each picture.

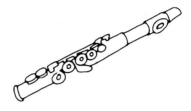

I. food
   flout
   flute
   float

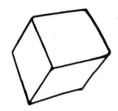

2. cube
   cub
   cool
   could

3. mull
   movie
   music
   mule

4. ton
   tuna
   tune
   town

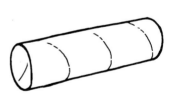

5. tube
   tuba
   truth
   troop

6. cub
   cuff
   cube
   costume

Now, write a complete sentence about one of the pictures.

_____

_____

Name _____

Write a vocabulary word on each line to replace the words in **dark print**.

> | | | |
> |---|---|---|
> | **bland** | **fiery** | **boasts** |
> | **claimed** | **open-air** | **citrus** |

1. Martin Luther King Jr. was **full of spirit** when he spoke, because his cause was so important to him.   _____

2. I **took as my own** my red hat from the lost-and-found box.   _____

3. Africa **has** the Nile River, which is the longest river in the world.   _____

4. This soup is **lacking in flavor,** so you should add some salt and pepper.   _____

5. My brother wants to live on a farm and grow **tart and sour** fruit.   _____

6. Uncle James likes to shop at the **outdoor** market on Saturday.   _____

voicesreading Grade 3

Name _____

Writing Dates, Times, and Places Correctly Follow these simple rules when writing dates, times, and places.

- Capitalize the first letter of the month.
  Always include a comma following the day.
  Example: November 10, 2005

- Always include a colon after the hour.
  Example: 4:00 A.M.

- Capitalize names of places.
  Example: Granville, Ohio
  Columbus Museum of Art

Answer the questions below. Be sure to follow the rules listed in the box.

I. What is today's date? _____

2. When is your birthday? _____

3. What is the name of the city and state where you were born?

   _____

4. What time do you wake up in the morning? _____

5. What is the name of your school? _____

6. What time do you arrive home from school? _____

7. What time do you go to bed at night?_____

8. What is the name of the library in your town? _____

Name _____

r-Controlled ar, or Look at the pictures. Write the word from the box that names each picture.

voicesreading Grade 3

farm	corn	shark	star
harp	store	horn	fork

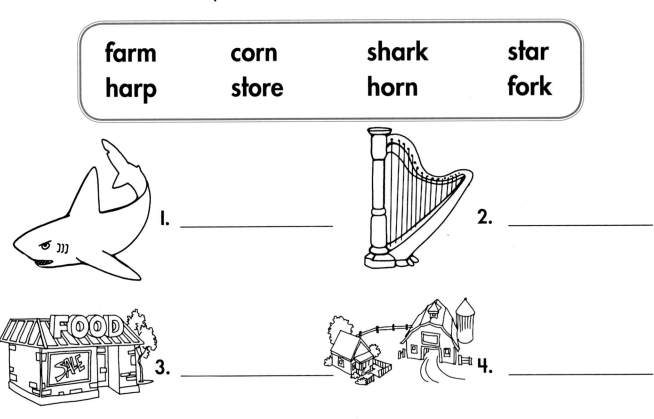

1. _____

2. _____

3. _____

4. _____

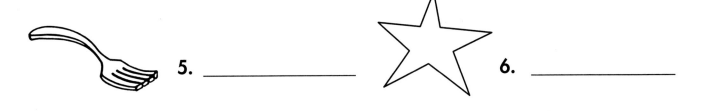

5. _____

6. _____

7. _____

8. _____

Name _____

Spelling Words

amuse	chute	confuse	dune	excuse	flute
fumes	fuse	June	mute	refuse	salute

Circle the hidden spelling words. Words may be spelled backward, forward, or diagonal.

```
B  C  O  N  F  U  S  E  L  P
D  S  E  M  U  F  O  H  S  A
U  C  M  O  J  U  N  E  A  M
N  U  H  B  U  S  A  T  L  U
E  X  C  U  S  E  L  U  U  S
A  F  L  U  T  E  T  M  T  E
R  E  F  U  S  E  K  I  E  B
```

voicesreading Grade 3

Name _____

How to Read a Diagram The **title** of a diagram tells the topic of the diagram. **Labels** provide more information about the topic. Look at the Venn diagram and answer the questions.

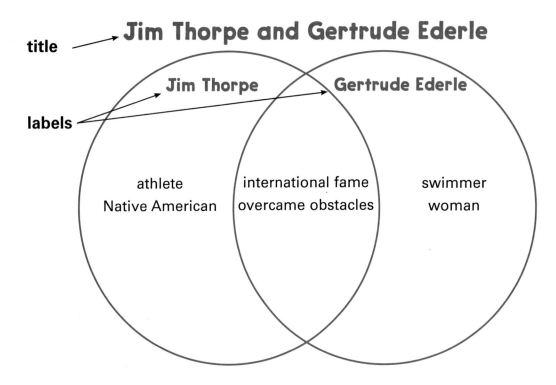

Jim Thorpe and Gertrude Ederle

title

labels

Jim Thorpe

Gertrude Ederle

athlete
Native American

international fame
overcame obstacles

swimmer
woman

voicesreading Grade 3

I. What is the title of the diagram? _____

2. What is the label for the first circle? _____

3. What is the label for the second circle? _____

4. Name two things Jim Thorpe and Gertrude Ederle have in common. _____

5. Name two things that were different about Jim Thorpe and Gertrude Ederle. _____

_____

Name _____

Science-Related Words Look at the list definitions in the box. Draw a line to match the scientist with the topic.

zoologist: a person who studies animals
botanist: a person who studies plants
astronomer: a person who studies stars, planets, and space
meteorologist: a person who studies weather
geologist: a person who studies Earth's layers
environmentalist: a person who studies the environment

Scientist   ## Topic

I. **botanist**   animals

2. **astronomer**   Earth's layers

3. **zoologist**   stars and planets

4. **geologist**   plants

5. **meteorologist**   weather

6. **environmentalist**   environment

Name _____

Draw a line from each vocabulary word to its definition.

I. sites   excellent

2. cope   a person who escapes
                                           to another country for
                                           protection

3. first-class   to do what is
                                           commanded

4. lacked   World Wide Web pages
                                           that have information
                                           about a topic

5. refugee   to get by

6. obey   did not have

voicesreading Grade 3

Copyright © Zaner-Bloser, Inc.

Name _____

Categorize and Classify Think about the story **My Name is Celia**. In the story, music is an important part of who Celia is. Think about things in your life that make you who you are. Make a list of these things.

Things I Enjoy Doing	Things I Do Well
_____	_____
_____	_____
_____	_____
_____	_____

Look at the lists you wrote. Are there ways you can share your gifts with others? Write two sentences that tell how you can use your gifts.

_____

_____

_____

_____

Name _____

Initials and Abbreviations Read each sentence. Write the abbreviations or initials from the box to replace the words in **dark print**.

Mr.	U.S.A	St.	Ave.	Jr.	Dr.
Hts.	Dec.	Jan.	Mon.	Wed.	Fri.

1. The brick house in Highland **Heights** belongs to my best friend's family. _____

2. **Doctor** Johnson does not work on weekends. _____

3. I have art class on **Monday, Wednesday,** and **Friday** this week. _____

4. Our vacation begins in **December** and ends in **January**. _____

5. There is a new book about giraffes by Thomas Bartlett **Junior** that I would like to read. _____

6. My teacher, **Mister** Whipple, was a spelling champion when he was my age. _____

7. Are you leaving the **United States of America** for vacation? _____

8. There are entrances to the school on College **Street** and on Granger **Avenue**. _____

voicesreading Grade 3

Copyright © Zaner-Bloser, Inc.

Name _____

What Did I Learn About Discrimination? What did you learn from the debate? Write down your thoughts and feelings below.

Things I Learned From the Debate

I. I was on the _____ team.

2. I was treated **fairly**   **unfairly**. (circle one)

3. During the debate, I felt _____

because _____

_____

_____

_____ .

4. Now that I know the teacher was intentionally treating the

teams differently, I feel _____

because _____

_____

_____

_____ .

Name _____

The u_e Pattern Shade the bubble next to the word that best completes each sentence.

I. We have a laundry _____ in the hallway for our dirty clothes.
   ○ chewed   ○ could   ○ chute   ○ choose

2. Lea sang in _____, even though she was nervous.
   ○ town   ○ tune   ○ took   ○ tout

3. Watching fish swimming in a tank can _____ a baby for hours.
   ○ amuse   ○ allow   ○ mood   ○ amount

4. The _____ kitten batted the toy across the room.
   ○ coop   ○ cute   ○ could   ○ croup

5. It is very _____ to talk when someone else is talking.
   ○ roomy   ○ round   ○ rouse   ○ rude

6. We try to _____ plastic bags when we go to the grocery store.
   ○ drink   ○ loose   ○ reuse   ○ rebound

7. The _____ spring water tasted cold and refreshing.
   ○ pure   ○ poor   ○ pour   ○ power

8. The _____ is that we have to recycle our plastic bottles.
   ○ room   ○ rowdy   ○ rude   ○ rule

9. We _____ our chess game every day at recess.
   ○ round   ○ resume   ○ room   ○ remove

10. The queen's hat was decorated with an ostrich _____.
   ○ plume   ○ pound   ○ pool   ○ plow

voicesreading Grade 3

Name _____

Circle the misspelled words in each sentence and write the words correctly on the lines.

1. Camilla likes to amuze herself by playing music on a flewt.

_____   _____

2. It is hot on the red sand dewn in the month of jun.

_____   _____

3. The smoke and feumes went up the chimney shoote and floated above the little cabin.

_____   _____

4. "There is no exkuse for that sloppy salut," said the sergeant to the soldier.

_____   _____

5. I refuze to touch the fuwz because it is dangerous.

_____   _____

6. A hard question might confuze me and make me meuwt in class.

_____   _____

Name _____

Using a Thesaurus Read the paragraph. Use a thesaurus to replace the words in **dark print** with more interesting words.

One (**1.**) **nice** day, I went for a (**2.**) **walk** with my grandmother.

The air felt (**3.**) **cool** and the leaves were (**4.**) **falling** from the trees.

A flock of birds (**5.**) **moved** overhead. Grandma (**6.**) **said** that the

birds were flying south. Many of our neighbors were raking

leaves into (**7.**) **big** piles. Oh, how I wanted to (**8.**) **run** and (**9.**) **jump**

into the leaves! As soon as we returned home, I (**10.**) **began** raking

my own pile.

1. _____   **2.** _____

3. _____   **4.** _____

5. _____   **6.** _____

7. _____   **8.** _____

9. _____   **10.** _____

Voicesreading Grade 3

Copyright © Zaner-Bloser, Inc.

Name _____

Write the vocabulary word that belongs in each group.

bland	fiery	boasts
claimed	open-air	citrus

1. flavorless, uninteresting, boring, _____

2. demanded, took, grabbed, _____

3. owns, possesses, has, _____

4. spirited, lively, passionate, _____

5. sour, tangy, pulpy, _____

6. outside, under the stars, unsheltered, _____

Now, write a sentence using two or three vocabulary words.

_____

_____

_____

_____

Name _____

Write the vocabulary word from the box that best completes each sentence.

voicesreading Grade 3

sites	first-class	lacked
cope	obey	refugee

1. The fancy, _____ hotel had a large swimming pool.

2. Owen's parents _____ a car, so they took the bus to the zoo.

3. The_____ left her home to live in a country that would protect her.

4. If you tell our dog to roll over, he will _____ your command.

5. The World Wide Web has many _____ with information about hiking and camping.

6. One way to _____ with our problems is to talk about them.

Copyright © Zaner-Bloser, Inc.

Name _____

Fact and Opinion Think about the story **My Name is Celia**. Write five facts and five opinions from the story.

voicesreading Grade 3

Facts

1. _____
   _____
   _____

2. _____
   _____
   _____

3. _____
   _____
   _____

4. _____
   _____
   _____

5. _____
   _____

Opinions

1. _____
   _____
   _____

2. _____
   _____
   _____

3. _____
   _____
   _____

4. _____
   _____
   _____

5. _____
   _____

Name _____

Draw Conclusions Think about the story **Ruby's Wish**. Complete the chart with details that support the conclusion in the top box.

Conclusion: Boys and girls were treated differently.

Detail:

Detail:

Detail:

voicesreading Grade 3

Copyright © Zaner-Bloser, Inc.

Name _____

The Schwa Sound Look at the first word in each line. Circle the word in the line that has the same sound as the letter in **dark print**.

1. wag**o**n   slot   bottom   angle   broke

2. **a**live   extra   crate   plant   aim

3. hum**a**n   hatch   hang   vocal   paint

4. pil**o**t   flock   broke   bacon   blown

5. met**a**l   oval   strange   clamp   frame

6. **a**bout   blast   umbrella   train   trace

7. op**e**n   fence   beast   given   free

8. m**o**ney   other   frost   snow   close

9. s**o**me   throne   love   cost   float

10. pand**a**   stage   became   again   blast

11. **a**bove   class   grain   maybe   animal

12. **a**fraid   slept   please   asleep   steep

Name _____

Complete the crossword puzzle with the vocabulary words from the box.

corral	trough	tuning
strummed	exasperated	noxious

Across
1. harmful to health
3. stroked the strings of an instrument
5. a long, narrow container for animal food or water
6. adjusting instruments so they have the correct pitch

Down
2. a fenced-in area for animals
4. annoyed and frustrated

Name _____

Keeping to the Point A good writer makes sure each sentence talks about the main idea of a paper. Read the paragraph about recess below. Cross out the sentences that do not belong.

Recess is one of the most important parts of the school day. Exercise keeps us healthy. Sliding and swinging are my favorite activities. After recess, we are able to focus on schoolwork more. We have a new soccer field behind the playground. Fresh air is good for clearing the mind, too. It's good that we have recess every day!

Name _____

The u_e Pattern Write a word from the box to match each clue.

plume	costume	exclude	flute	mule	prune
compute	spruce	perfume	resume	truce	rude

1. This is a musical instrument. _____

2. This is a type of tree. _____

3. This is a pleasant-smelling liquid. _____

4. This is an outfit worn for fun. _____

5. This is an agreement to stop fighting. _____

6. This means the opposite of **polite**. _____

7. To cut branches is to do this. _____

8. This means "to start again." _____

9. This is an animal. _____

10. This is a fluffy feather. _____

11. To leave out is to do this. _____

12. To find a math answer is to do this. _____

Name _____

Spelling Words

upon	collar	animal	wagon	about	tonight
never	tractor	above	another	tomorrow	couple

Write the spelling words in **ABC order** on the lines.

1. _____   2. _____

3. _____   4. _____

5. _____   6. _____

7. _____   8. _____

9. _____   10. _____

11. _____   12. _____

Name _____

> **Skim and Scan** **Skimming** is looking quickly at text. When skimming, look over section headings, chapter titles, illustrations, boxes and sidebars, boldfaced words, and other items that stand out on the page. Be sure to read the first paragraph on a page and the first sentence of the other paragraphs.
>
> **Scanning** is reading quickly down a page, looking for the main facts or key words and phrases.

Use a book from your classroom to answer the questions.

1. Skim through the book. Are there section heads and chapters in the book? _____

2. Are there words in **dark print** that stand out? _____

3. Do the pictures or illustrations give you an idea of what the book is about? _____

4. Scan the first page. What are the main facts or key words that you read?

   _____

   _____

   _____

   _____

   _____

voicesreading Grade 3

Copyright © Zaner-Bloser, Inc.

Name _____

Persuasive Read this example of a persuasive essay about recess.

I think it is important that we have more time for recess. More recess is good for teachers and students.

Students need more time to exercise. Eating well isn't the only way to be healthy. Getting exercise helps, too. When people exercise, they focus better on things such as studying.

Longer recess helps teachers, too. Teachers would have more time to catch up on their work. It would be easier to teach students. Then teachers could go home earlier. I hope you will carefully consider my request to give us a longer recess.

Name _____

Related Words—Math Write each word in **dark print** from the box in the correct column.

addition: the combination of two or more numbers to get one number

calculator: a machine that does addition, subtraction, multiplication, and division

cylinder: a form with one curved side and two equal circular sides

multiplication: a number added to itself a number of times to make another number

pentagon: a shape with five sides

scale: a device that measures weight

Things We Do in Math	Shapes We See in Math	Tools We Use in Math
_____	_____	_____
_____	_____	_____

Now, write a sentence about something you've learned in math class. Try to use as many words from the box as possible.

_____

_____

_____

Name _____

Write a vocabulary word from the box to match each definition.

> **buckboard** **tilted** **polished**
> **blustery** **campaign** **exemplified**

1. an open carriage with four wheels and an attached seat _____

2. shown by example _____

3. planned sets of military actions undertaken to achieve a goal in war _____

4. leaned _____

5. made shiny by rubbing _____

6. cold and windy _____

voicesreading Grade 3

Name _____

Draw Conclusions Think about the story **Ruby's Wish**. Answer the questions.

1. Why did Ruby's ears turn red when the teacher praised her?

   _____

2. Why did Ruby have to work harder than the boys?

   _____

   _____

   _____

3. Why did the mothers think studying was not important for girls?

   _____

   _____

   _____

4. Why do you think Ruby noticed the fish gulping for air under the ice?

   _____

   _____

   _____

voicesreading Grade 3

Name _____

Prepositional Phrases Look at the picture. Write the prepositional phrase from the box that best completes each sentence.

on the blanket	on the branch	in a basket
under the table	over the park	behind my friend

I. The bird perches _____ and sings a song.

2. The hungry dog crouches _____, hoping for some food scraps.

3. We hear the jet's engine roar as it flies _____.

4. The kittens snuggle together _____.

5. I wait in line _____.

6. My brother naps _____.

Name _____

Persuasion Map You can use a Persuasion Map to organize your ideas for your essay.

voicesreading Grade 3

Facts/Examples

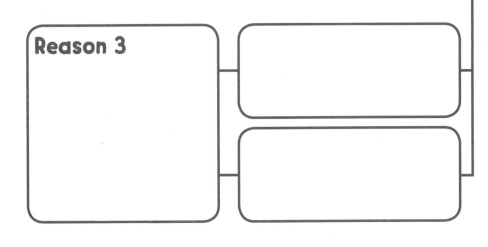

Reason 1

Reason 2

Reason 3

Call to Action

Name _____

Speaking Out Against Unfair Treatment Think about a time when you or someone you know was treated unfairly. What would you say if you could speak to the person who was being unfair? Complete the sentences below.

I. The time when I or someone else was treated unfairly was

_____

_____

_____ .

2. At the time, I felt _____

_____

_____

_____ .

3. Something I would say to the person who was being unfair is

_____

_____

_____

_____ .

Name _____

The Schwa Sound Circle the three words in each row that have the schwa sound. If you need help, use a dictionary.

1.	wonder	planted	lunch	buzz	open
2.	banana	chanted	today	muddy	young
3.	silly	tonight	uncle	drum	above
4.	upon	soggy	model	moldy	mother
5.	other	afraid	cloth	tomorrow	fresh
6.	asleep	sound	youth	agree	couple
7.	alarm	animal	again	foam	fume
8.	bacon	check	broke	taken	wagon
9.	done	gorilla	drone	around	about
10.	another	seven	award	wait	wash

Name _____

Spelling Words

about	above	animal	another	collar	couple
never	tomorrow	tonight	tractor	upon	wagon

Unscramble the letters in **dark print** to spell words from the box. Write the words correctly on the lines.

l. **ponu** _____

2. **verne** _____

3. **therano** _____

4. **tuoba** _____

5. **bovea** _____

6. **tortrac** _____

7. **rowtomor** _____

8. **nightto** _____

9. **larcol** _____

l0. **nimala** _____

ll. **plecou** _____

l2. **gonaw** _____

Name _____

Related Words—Science Read the list of scientists and their jobs in the box. Write the name of the scientist who could answer each question on the line.

> **botanist:** a person who studies plants
> **astronomer:** a person who studies stars, planets, and space
> **zoologist:** a person who studies animals
> **geologist:** a person who studies Earth's layers
> **environmentalist:** a person who studies the environment
> **meteorologist:** a person who studies weather

1. Will it be sunny tomorrow? _____

2. What does a sloth eat? _____

3. Which planet is closest to Earth? _____

4. What does poison ivy look like? _____

5. Is it better for the earth to use paper or plastic bags? _____

6. What are baby lions called? _____

7. What are clouds? _____

8. Why are leaves green? _____

voicesreading Grade 3

Name _____

Use this checklist when you revise your writing.

Revising Checklist: Persuasive

yes	no	Does the essay explain the opinion in the first and last paragraphs?
yes	no	Is the summary of reasons in the first paragraph?
yes	no	Is each reason listed in the order of importance?
yes	no	Do all details, examples, and reasons keep to the point?
yes	no	Does every sentence begin with a capital letter and end with correct punctuation?
yes	no	Are the prepositional phrases written correctly?

Name _____

Use the vocabulary words from the box to complete the paragraph.

corral	**trough**	**tuning**
strummed	**exasperated**	**noxious**

I went to the _____ to find Snicker, my favorite

horse. Snicker was drinking from the _____

when I got there. The water looked _____, but he

didn't seem to mind. Aunt Andie wanted me to walk to the store

to get some oats. When I arrived at the store, a man was

_____ his guitar. He _____ the

guitar and gave me an _____ look.

"I need new strings," he sighed.

So he hummed a song instead.

Name _____

Circle the vocabulary word that best completes each sentence.

I. I wore my hat, gloves, and a coat because it was a _____ day.

    blustery   **soggy**   **sweltering**   **monotone**

2. She will have to use the _____ to drive the children school.

    campaign   **citrus**   **wardrobe**   **buckboard**

3. The rider _____ the bike as he raced around the corner.

    tilted   **strummed**   **polished**   **vexed**

4. Fala _____ good manners when she opened the door for me.

    exasperated   **unplugged**   **exemplified**   **teetered**

5. The military _____ to liberate the country began by enlisting new soldiers.

    buckboard   **menu**   **campaign**   **vibration**

6. My brother _____ his car today so it would be shiny.

    exemplified   **polished**   **strummed**   **shamed**

Theme 4: Social Awareness   **81**

Name _____

Categorize and Classify Think about the story **Ruby's Wish**. List the things that the boys did under **Boys**. Then list the things that girls did under **Girls**.

Boys	Girls
_____	_____
_____	_____
_____	_____
_____	_____
_____	_____

How do you feel about the way girls and boys were treated?

_____

_____

_____

_____

voicesreading Grade 3

Name _____

Beginning, Middle, and End Think about the story **Uncle Jed's Barbershop**. Complete the chart with events from the story.

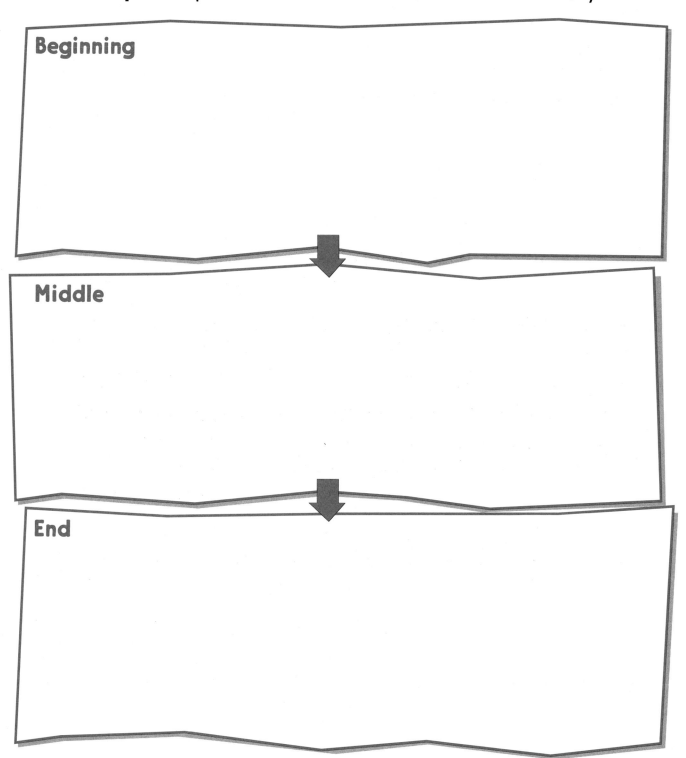

Beginning

Middle

End

Name _____

Long o Spelled o Read each sentence. Write the words that have the **long o** sound spelled **o** on the line.

1. My neighbor's dog was nowhere to be found. _____

2. I said that I would hang signs on the telephone poles. _____

3. Almost all of the folks in our complex helped search for the dog. _____

4. The poor, lost dog was cold and tired. _____

5. Nobody could believe that he had survived so long without food. _____

6. The next day, the local vet checked him to make sure he was all right. _____

voicesreading Grade 3

Name _____

Draw a line to match each vocabulary word in **dark print** to its definition.

1. rundown

an agreement with a company that it will pay for loss in return for regular payments

2. forcefully

a group of electronic or digital products

3. insurance

in poor condition

4. dear

in a powerful manner

5. technology

an amount of money saved for a special reason

6. fund

a loved person

voicesreading Grade 3

Copyright © Zaner-Bloser, Inc.

Name _____

Exaggeration Writers use **exaggeration** to make a story more interesting. A writer can make a person or thing seem bigger, better, or more important than it really is by exaggeration.

Example: (**Normal**) I like bananas.
(**Exaggeration**) I love bananas more than anything else in the world.

Read the paragraph below. Circle the phrases that are exaggerations.

I am going to build the best clubhouse in the world with my friend Parker. It will be so tall, we'll be able to reach out and touch the clouds. It will have three rooms, one just to keep thousands of buckets of candy. The best part will be the indoor basketball court. It's going to be one cool clubhouse!

voicesreading Grade 3

Name _____

The Schwa Sound Read the words in each tic-tac-toe board. Draw a line through the three words in each board that have the **schwa** sound. If you need help, use a dictionary.

I.

never	door	poke
other	bone	done
couple	don't	love

2.

butter	local	turn
button	cover	boil
cotton	love	alone

3.

other	lost	otter
couch	summer	such
trouble	broken	song

4.

study	upon	truth
tune	animal	trust
punt	afraid	soon

Name _____

Spelling Words

| below | close | clover | crow | fellow | flow |
| grocery | grown | hotel | pillow | solo | window |

Circle the hidden spelling words.

```
D   E   S   U   P   Y   H   O   K   W
G   R   O   W   N   F   L   O   W   I
R   O   L   E   U   E   O   U   R   N
O   H   O   T   E   L   O   T   C   D
C   A   Y   B   I   L   O   R   L   O
E   P   A   T   L   O   O   T   O   W
R   B   E   L   O   W   B   U   S   P
Y   P   I   L   L   O   W   H   E   R
A   B   F   K   D   G   G   C   U   S
C   L   O   V   E   R   E   A   T   S
```

voicesreading Grade 3

Name _____

Rereading for Information Read the paragraph about geckos.

The gecko is an interesting animal. It is the only lizard that has a voice. A gecko makes a squeaking or clicking noise that sounds like "gecko." Geckos have sticky toe pads so they can climb upside-down. Geckos are carnivores: they eat insects, birds, eggs, and tiny mammals. They hunt at night, which makes them nocturnal. Though their habitats are warm climates, geckos are found all over the world. Many people like them as pets, too.

Write two unfamiliar words from the paragraph.

I. _____   2. _____

Reread the paragraph. Write words or phrases from the paragraph that help you understand what these unfamiliar words mean.

I. _____

2. _____

Name _____

Dividing CVCVC Words Divide the word **after the consonant** if the first vowel is **short**.

Examples: cam/el   riv/er

Divid the word **after the first vowel** if the first vowel is **long**.

Examples: pi/lot   o/pen

voicesreading Grade 3

Write the words from the box in **ABC order**. Draw a line between the syllables.

| medal | even | basin | oval | magic | novel |
| fever | river | seven | talon | below | comet |

1. _____ 2. _____ 3. _____

4. _____ 5. _____ 6. _____

7. _____ 8. _____ 9. _____

10. _____ 11. _____ 12. _____

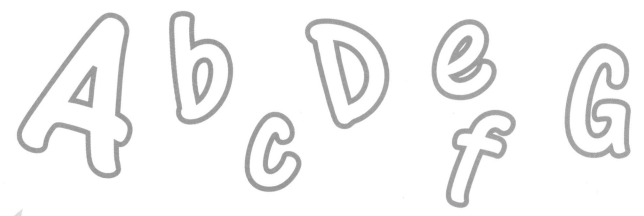

Name _____

Write the vocabulary word from the box that matches each definition.

settled	cheerily	pulsed
efficiently	chuckled	flurry

1. beat; throbbed _____

2. in a faster and easier way _____

3. laughed quietly _____

4. a sudden burst _____

5. decided upon _____

6. happily; in good spirits _____

Name _____

Beginning, Middle, and End Read the events from **Ruby's Wish**. If the event happened in the **beginning,** write **B**. If the event happened in the **middle,** write **M**. If the event happened at the **end,** write **E**.

I. The teacher praises Ruby for her calligraphy.   _____

2. Ruby is one of the university's first female students.   _____

3. Ruby has a talk with her grandfather.   _____

4. Ruby writes a poem about boys and girls.   _____

5. Ruby's grandfather hires a teacher.   _____

6. Ruby is accepted at the university.   _____

7. The girls stop going to class.   _____

8. Ruby lives in a house with many cousins.   _____

voicesreading Grade 3

Name _____

Identifying Negatives and Avoiding Double Negatives

Circle the negative word or words in each sentence. If the sentence has double negatives, rewrite the sentence correctly on the line.

I. Yesterday, I saw something I had not never seen.

_____

2. A little bird with no feathers had fallen out of a tree.

_____

3. Its mother was not nowhere in sight.

_____

4. I didn't not know what to do, so I ran to tell my mom.

_____

5. She said we should not touch the baby bird.

_____

6. The vet said we shouldn't never take the bird away from its nest.

_____

Name _____

My Dreams and Goals What dream or goal would you like to share with someone? Write a letter to that person describing your dream or goal.

Dear _____,

_____

_____

_____

_____

_____

_____

_____

_____,

_____

voicesreading Grade 3

Name _____

Long o Spelled o Circle the word that names each picture.

1.

goat
follow
flower
volcano

2.

Ohio
otter
closet
towel

3.

clown
bottom
point
grocery

4.

body
shower
cold
floss

5.

old
flower
blouse
toss

6.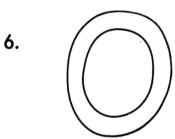

love
zero
sound
open

7.

boat
without
door
stroll

8.

phone
pole
piano
pillow

Name _____

Spelling Words

| below | close | clover | crow | fellow | flow |
| grocery | grown | hotel | pillow | solo | window |

Circle the misspelled words and write them correctly on the lines below.

I stand quietly in the hoetel looking out the large windowe.

A crowe perches cloce bellowe. It sits on a bench next to a fello

crow. I also see people floe in and out of a grosary store. When I

look up, I see clouds in the sky that look like clovur. "When I am

groan, I will fly soulo to see the clouds up close," I think to myself.

Then Mom says it's time for bed. I lay my head on the pillou,

close my eyes, and dream.

1. _____
2. _____
3. _____

4. _____
5. _____
6. _____

7. _____
8. _____
9. _____

10. _____
11. _____
12. _____

voicesreading Grade 3

Name _____

Related Words—Math Write the math word from the box that matches each example.

calculator	multiplication	watch	fraction
pattern	addition	subtraction	division

Things We Do in Math

1. 20 − 10 = 10 _____

2. 10 ÷ 5 = 2 _____

3. 3 x 3 = 9 _____

4. 7 + 8 = 15 _____

Things We Use in Math

5.  _____

6.  _____

7.  _____

8. _____

Name _____

Write a vocabulary word on each line to replace the words in **dark print**.

voicesreading Grade 3

dear	**insurance**	**technology**
fund	**rundown**	**forcefully**

1. Be a **loved person,** and help me wrap
these gifts. _____

2. The house is **in poor condition,** but with
some work, it will be beautiful. _____

3. If you drive, you must have **an agreement
with a company that it will pay for
loss in return for regular payments**. _____

4. The police officer charged into the store
in a powerful manner, catching the thief
in the act. _____

5. **A group of electronic and digital products**
in hospitals helps doctors and nurses
care for patients. _____

6. The school will open the **money saved
for a special reason** so the students
can have a new playground. _____

Copyright © Zaner-Bloser, Inc.

Name _____

Circle the vocabulary word that best completes each sentence.

1. There is a _____ of activity around an airplane before it is ready to take off.

   efficiently   **flurry**   **pulsed**   **jiffy**

2. I _____ because the movie was funny.

   chuckled   **settled**   **strummed**   **sneered**

3. We finally _____ our disagreement and shook hands.

   unplugged   **settled**   **unrivaled**   **campaigned**

4. He _____ walked home on the bright, sunny day.

   vibrations   **hauled**   **drafty**   **cheerily**

5. The crowded street _____ with excitement on New Year's Eve.

   exemplified   **settled**   **pulsed**   **urged**

6. Marie found she could study more _____ in her room.

   settled   **majesty**   **efficiently**   **eerily**

Name _____

Draw Conclusions Think about the story **Uncle Jed's Barbershop**. Answer the questions.

I. Why do you think Uncle Jed was Sarah Jean's favorite relative?

_____

_____

2. What was life like during the Great Depression?

_____

_____

_____

3 Why did so many people visit Uncle Jed's new barbershop when it opened?

_____

_____

_____

4. Why does Sarah Jean believe her Uncle Jed died a happy man?

_____

_____

voicesreading Grade 3

Name _____

Ask and Answer Questions Think about the story **Uncle Jed's Barbershop**. Circle the correct answer for each question.

1. What type of writing did the author use in the book?

   biography   **personal narrative**   **story**   **report**

2. Who is telling the story?

   Daddy   **Uncle Jed**   **Sarah Jean**   **Mommy**

3. Which is an example of **exaggeration**?

   Uncle Jed was the only black barber in the county.

   The floors were so clean you could eat off of them.

   Three hundred dollars was a lot of money in those days.

   On opening day, people came from all over the county.

4. Why is the setting of the story so important?

   _____

   _____

5. Why do you think the author chose to write the story in the style that she did?

   _____

   _____

voicesreading Grade 3

Copyright © Zaner-Bloser, Inc.

Name _____

Long e Spelled ie Write a word from the box to complete each sentence.

voicesreading Grade 3

grief	niece	achieve	piece	stories
cookies	relieved	brief	believe	movie

1. My aunt gave me a _____ of cherry pie for dessert.

2. She smiled and said I was her favorite _____.

3. I _____ she was the person who taught me how to tie my shoes.

4. She took me to see a _____ about a horse that won a race.

5. I was so _____ when the horse won, that I cried.

6. The moral of the story was that if you tried your best, you could _____ anything.

7. After the show, we stopped for hot cocoa and _____.

8. It was a _____ walk home from the theater.

Copyright © Zaner-Bloser, Inc.

Name _____

Write the vocabulary word from the box that goes with each definition.

soggy	unplugged	tinker
repair	version	catalog

I. a book or pamphlet with items that can be ordered

_____

2. something slightly different from the original

_____

3. to make something work again

_____

4. to make a casual attempt to fix

_____

5. removed from source of electricity

_____

6. soaked with moisture

_____

Theme 4: Social Awareness **103**

voicesreading Grade 3

Name _____

Long o Spelled o Read the words in each row. Circle the words that have a **long o** sound spelled **o**.

1. polar	plow	cross	stone	stout
2. cozy	throw	shout	town	stomp
3. billow	sold	slouch	float	cow
4. motor	mouse	brown	moldy	moss
5. focus	flock	frozen	crouch	towel
6. broken	potion	plop	would	brought
7. snowy	floppy	crowd	soon	voted
8. chosen	done	upon	folder	found
9. below	should	shower	closet	host
10. crow	frown	probe	money	flood
11. stolen	gold	story	sour	shoe
12. joke	frog	jolly	phone	block

Name _____

Spelling Words

| belief | believe | brief | chief | field | grief |
| niece | piece | shield | thief | wield | yield |

Unscramble the letters in **dark print** to spell words from the box. Write the words correctly on the lines.

1. **yiedl** _____

2. **fieth** _____

3. **cepie** _____

4. **riefg** _____

5. **fiech** _____

6. **lievebe** _____

7. **liefbe** _____

8. **frieb** _____

9. **ifeld** _____

10. **cenie** _____

11. **ldiesh** _____

12. **ieldw** _____

voicesreading Grade 3

Name _____

Special Plural Nouns Read each sentence. Circle the word that correctly completes each sentence.

I. She broke the bread into two (**half, halves**).

2. There were so many (**people, person**) in the crowd, I couldn't find you!

3. I lost my two front (**teeth, tooth**) when I was in the first grade.

4. The (**child, children**) were happy when school was over for the year.

5. We watched a flock of (**goose, geese**) fly overhead.

6. My aunt doesn't like (**mice, mouse**).

7. I am going to knit (**scarf, scarves**) for everyone.

8. Mom plays soccer with other (**woman, women**).

9. We baked several (**loaves, loaf**) of bread.

10. My grandfather is more than six (**foot, feet**) tall.

II. We raked a pile of (**leaf, leaves**) in the yard.

12. Mr. Torres is one of the (**man, men**) who works with my uncle.

Name _____

How Can We Overcome Obstacles and Pursue Our Dreams? Think about the stories you have read. What obstacles did the characters have? How did they overcome the obstacles? Choose two characters from the stories in the box and write a short paragraph comparing how they overcame their obstacles.

> **Jim Thorpe's Bright Path**
> **America's Champion Swimmer: Gertrude Ederle**
> **My Name is Celia**
> **Ruby's Wish**
> **Uncle Jed's Barbershop**

Characters: _____ **and** _____

_____

_____

_____

_____

_____

_____

voicesreading Grade 3

Name _____

Long e Spelled ie Read the words in each tic-tac-toe board. Draw a line through the three words in each board that have the have the **long e** sound spelled **ie**.

1.

necktie	pie	field
spread	brief	sweat
shield	spy	free

2.

belief	good-bye	bread
cry	piece	die
head	street	grief

3.

chief	wield	thief
weep	ready	chef
stead	tread	creep

4.

east	head	niece
welcome	plead	believe
yes	lean	yield

Name _____

Circle the misspelled words in each sentence and write the words correctly on the lines.

I. I saw the theef for a bref moment before he ran away.

_____   _____

2. We baleave the police officer should be the new chiaf.

_____   _____

3. My nese feels greif when she sees stray cats.

_____   _____

4. She found a pease of the kite in the feild.

_____   _____

5. It is my baleaf that drivers should yeald to people crossing the street.

_____   _____

6. A knight must be able to weald a heavy chield.

_____   _____

Name _____

Spelling Words

grief	shield	yield	belief	wield	chief
believe	piece	brief	field	niece	thief

Write the spelling words in **ABC order**.

1. _____

2. _____

3. _____

4. _____

5. _____

6. _____

7. _____

8. _____

9. _____

10. _____

11. _____

12. _____

voicesreading Grade 3

Copyright © Zaner-Bloser, Inc.

Name _____

Write a vocabulary word on each line to complete the sentences.

| soggy | unplugged | tinker |
| repair | version | catalog |

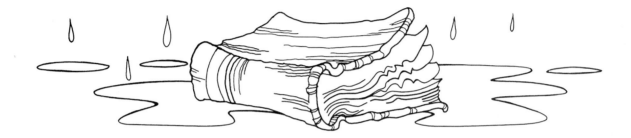

1. The book was _____ after I left it out in the rain.

2. Stores will sell a new _____ of the game in March.

3. Dad orders his shoes from a _____ because he does not like to shop in stores.

4. A mechanic came out to _____ the airplane before takeoff.

5. My brother likes to _____ with his car on the weekends.

6. We _____ the lamps before we left on our trip.

Name _____

Author's Viewpoint Think about the story **Secret Signs.**
Complete the web with clues about the author's viewpoint.

Clue 1:

Clue 2:

Author's Viewpoint:
Slavery is wrong.

Clue 3:

Clue 4:

Name _____

Words Ending With -ed, -ing Add **-ed** and **-ing** to each word and write the new word on the line. (**Hint:** You will have to change some of the endings before adding **-ed** or **-ing**.)

	Add -ed	Add -ing
1. jump		
2. believe		
3. talk		
4. skate		
5. taste		
6. hurry		
7. bake		
8. stack		
9. study		
10. blame		
11. scare		
12. carry		
13. splash		
14. thank		

Name _____

Draw a line from each definition on the left to the vocabulary word in **dark print** that matches on the right.

I. something that limits

involved

2. an uneasy or troubled time

overheard

3. heard accidentally

unrest

4. money left over after
   expenses have been paid

restriction

5. the crime of plotting against
   one's country during war

profit

6. included; contained as a part

treason

Now, write complete sentences using the vocabulary words.

7. _____

8. _____

9. _____

10. _____

II. _____

12. _____

voicesreading Grade 3

Copyright © Zaner-Bloser, Inc.

Name _____

Varying Sentence Types Paragraphs that have statements, exclamations, and questions are interesting to read.

Example: (Original) It was a bad day after my dog ate my homework. My pants ripped when they got caught on the school bus door. Everything went wrong today.

(With varying sentences) Have you ever had a day where nothing goes right? This morning, my dog ate my homework! Then, my pants ripped on the school bus door. Uhhh! What else could go wrong?

Write a short paragraph about someone who found money on the ground. Be sure to vary your sentences.

Name _____

Long e Spelled ie Circle the word in each row that has the **long e** sound spelled **ie**.

voicesreading Grade 3

1. tree	sled	field	spread	spied
2. please	chief	pebble	cried	bread
3. fleece	fence	thread	movie	tried
4. steam	fly	good-bye	grief	breakfast
5. creepy	achieve	ride	meant	died
6. sweet	flies	cookie	tread	several
7. reach	belief	health	credit	pies
8. seen	best	example	wield	lied
9. beach	break	pester	piece	necktie
10. wheat	ever	niece	head	second
11. theme	threat	then	thief	best
12. clean	yield	better	fried	been

Name _____

Spelling Words

becoming	borrowed	cleaning	clearing
dawdled	feeding	printed	reading
swimming	tripped	wrapped	yawning

Circle the hidden spelling words from the box.

```
B  R  C  L  E  A  R  I  N  G  F
O  E  F  D  U  X  A  L  G  P  E
R  A  C  H  P  O  Y  N  W  R  E
R  D  P  O  U  D  I  J  R  I  D
O  I  K  U  M  M  N  O  A  N  I
W  N  O  T  M  I  Z  A  P  T  N
E  G  E  I  J  L  N  N  P  E  G
D  A  W  D  L  E  D  G  E  D  H
G  S  Y  A  N  G  G  A  D  Q  P
Y  A  W  N  I  N  G  D  A  R  K
T  R  I  P  P  E  D  D  A  I  S
C  L  E  A  N  I  N  G  M  O  O
```

voicesreading Grade 3

Name _____

Adjusting Your Reading Rate People read at different speeds. You may read something that is easy to understand faster than text that is harder to understand. If you are being tested on something, you may read that information more slowly.

Read each sentence below. Tell whether you might read it at a **slow, medium,** or **fast** rate. Then, tell why you chose that rate.

I. Read the sentence. Circle the words that rhyme. Underline the words with the same vowel sound.

_____

_____

2. Children's Menu: chicken fingers, cheeseburger, macaroni and cheese

_____

_____

3. The following information will be on the test: names of states, capitals, rivers, and oceans.

_____

_____

4. Skim through the book to see if it looks interesting.

_____

_____

Copyright © Zaner-Bloser, Inc.

Name _____

Narrative   Read this example of a story about two children who help someone.

Rachel and Kylie were good friends. They lived next to one another. They always rode the bus to school together. One day, they got on the bus and sat down. Rachel and Kylie opened their science books to study for the big test. As the bus started to move, they heard someone sobbing. Kylie looked behind the seat. Megan, a girl in their class, was crying.

"Why are you crying?" Rachel asked Megan.

"I forgot to study for the test," Megan replied.

"We will help you!" Kylie and Rachel exclaimed together.

Kylie and Rachel took turns quizzing Megan. When they arrived at school, Megan felt much better. After school, they saw her again. She was smiling because she passed the test!

Name _____

Inflected Forms Circle the inflected word that best completes each sentence.

1. Yesterday at my swim meet, I swam (**best, better**) than I swam last week.

2. I wasn't the (**faster, fastest**) swimmer, but I beat all of my records.

3. I was happy because I (**dived, diving**) better than ever, too.

4. My coach was (**happier, happiest**) with my performance than she'd ever been.

5. She (**told, telling**) me to keep up the good work.

6. Mom (**took, taken**) me out for dinner after the swim meet.

Add an ending to the word in **dark print** so each sentence makes sense. Write the new word on the line.

7. This has been the **hot** summer I can remember in a long time. _____

8. I am **happy** when I am at the beach with a good book. _____

9. My mom **smile** at me when I helped my sister with her homework. _____

10. I am **go** to the park for a nice, long hike later today. _____

11. When the movie was over, I sat and **wait** for a few minutes. _____

12. I **forget** to feed the dog before I went to school yesterday. _____

voicesreading Grade 3

Copyright © Zaner-Bloser, Inc.

Name _____

Draw a line to match each vocabulary word in **dark print** to its definition.

1. **treaty**
the examination of statements or events by a court

2. **respond**
polished

3. **shined**
moved back

4. **trenches**
to answer

5. **retreated**
deep ditches used for hiding soldiers during battle

6. **trial**
an agreement for peace

Name _____

Author's Viewpoint Answer the questions about the story **Secret Signs**. Write your answers on the lines.

I. How does the author feel about Luke and his mother?

_____

_____

2. What does the author think about the slave catchers?

_____

_____

3. How do you know the author feels that way?

_____

_____

4. What does the author mean when she writes, "Look toward the light"?

_____

_____

voicesreading Grade 3

Name _____

Making the Subject and Verb Agree Proofread the paragraph. Make sure the subject and verb agree in each sentence. Circle the words that are incorrect and rewrite them correctly on the lines.

My dog, Daisy, spend her entire day barking at squirrels and trucks. It seem like other dogs passes their time doing quiet activities. Why doesn't my dog buries bones like the other dogs? My friend's dog, Digger, hide bones every day! I thinks that digging is normal dog behavior. I know Daisy believe she is protecting us, but her barking really annoy me!

1. _____   2. _____

3. _____   4. _____

5. _____   6. _____

7. _____   8. _____

Name _____

Storyboard You can use a Storyboard to organize the ideas for your story.

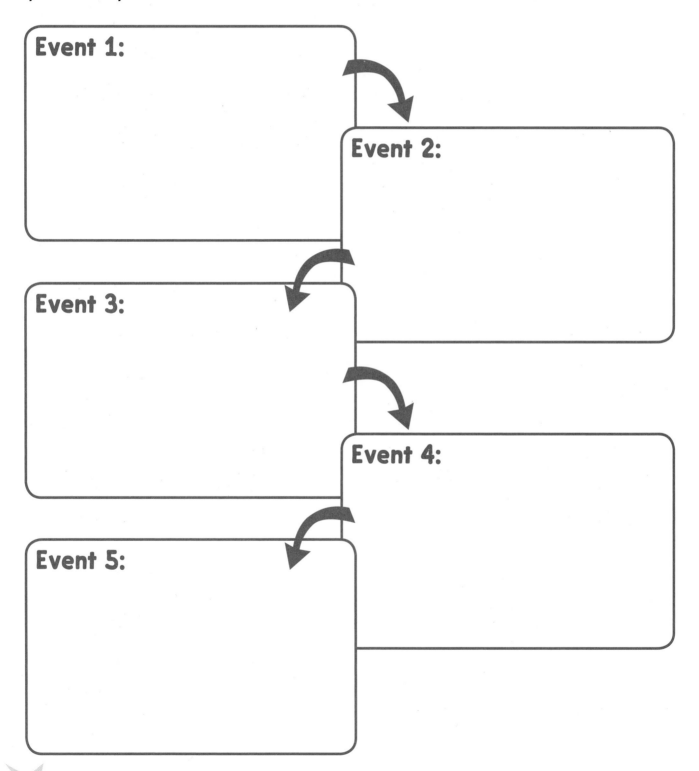

Event 1:

Event 2:

Event 3:

Event 4:

Event 5:

Name _____

My Personal Goal Think about the goals you talked about with your family and classmates. Complete the sentences below. Then share your answers with your partner.

My Goal

1. Three things I want to learn or do in the next few

   months are _____

   _____

   _____

   _____ .

2. The one goal I chose is _____

   _____

   _____ .

3. Three reasons I chose this goal are _____

   _____

   _____

   _____ .

Name _____

Words Ending With -ed, -ing Choose a word from the box to complete each sentence. Add **-ed** or **-ing** to the word and write the word on the line. (**Hint:** You will have to change the spelling before adding an ending to some words.)

| save | swim | sled | call | poke |
| snap | call | skate | hurry | hop |

1. Sarah _____ her grandmother to wish her a happy birthday.

2. I will be _____ in our new pool all summer this year.

3. A frog _____ along the trail and into the woods.

4. My cousin is _____ her fingers to the beat of the music.

5. I _____ home after school because Grandpa was coming over for dinner.

6. The children were _____ on the pond last weekend.

7. Do you want to go _____ if there is enough snow?

8. I am _____ all of my allowance so I can buy a new bike.

voicesreading Grade 3

Copyright © Zaner-Bloser, Inc.

Name _____

Circle the misspelled words and write them correctly on the lines below.

Yesterday, Dad told us, "After you have finished reeding your book, kleening your room, and feading the dog, we can go to the pool."

Things didn't start off so well. First, Diego borowed one of my suits because he couldn't find his. I made sure I prented my name in it so he wouldn't try to keep it. Then, as we walked to the swiming pool, Diego dautled all the way there. i actually caught him yauning as if he were bored! I said to myself, "It is bekumming clear that someone doesn't want to go to the pool!"

When we were almost there, Diego triped on a big rock in the clearring. Then he rapped his arms around Dad and wouldn't let go. Swimming alone wasn't any fun, so we didn't stay at the pool very long. What a day!

I. _____ 2. _____

3. _____ 4. _____

5. _____ 6. _____

7. _____ 8. _____

9. _____ 10. _____

II. _____ 12. _____

Name _____

Dividing CVCVC Words Look at the words in the box. Write the words in **ABC order** and draw a line between the syllables in each word.

label	cabin	lemon	music	salad	pupil
fever	siren	tiger	wagon	petal	robin

1. _____

2. _____

3. _____

4. _____

5. _____

6. _____

7. _____

8. _____

9. _____

10. _____

11. _____

12. _____

Name _____

Use this checklist when you revise your writing.

Revising Checklist: Narrative

yes	**no**	Does my story have an interesting plot, characters, and setting?
yes	**no**	Is there a clear beginning, middle, and end to the story?
yes	**no**	Do time-order words tell when events happened?
yes	**no**	Are there several different types of sentences, and do they belong in the story?
yes	**no**	Does dialogue make the characters seem real to the readers?
yes	**no**	Does my story have descriptions of people, places, and things?
yes	**no**	Does every sentence begin with a capital letter and end with the correct punctuation?
yes	**no**	Does the subject and verb agree in every sentence?

voicesreading Grade 3

Name _____

Write the vocabulary word from the box that best completes each sentence.

profit	restriction	unrest
involved	treason	overheard

I. I _____ my parents talking about my report card last night.

2. The train has a _____ on the number of bags you may carry.

3. The county has been in a state of _____ since insects destroyed the crops.

4. What is _____ in joining the chess club?

5. I made a small _____ on my lemonade sales this summer.

6. The court found the spy guilty of _____.

Name _____

Write the vocabulary word from the box that replaces the words in **dark print**. Write the word on the line.

> **trenches   retreated   treaty   shined   respond   trial**

1. The government signed a **peace agreement** with the Native Americans. _____

2. It is important that you **give an answer** to an invitation. _____

3. Many soldiers had to live in **deep ditches used for hiding during battle** during World War I. _____

4. A judge must preside over the **examination of statements or events by a court**. _____

5. I **moved back** into the house when I saw that it was raining outside. _____

6. It is important to keep your shoes **polished** if you want them to look their best. _____

voicesreading Grade 3

Name _____

Beginning, Middle, and End Think about the story **Secret Signs**. Tell what happens at the **beginning, middle,** and **end** of the story.

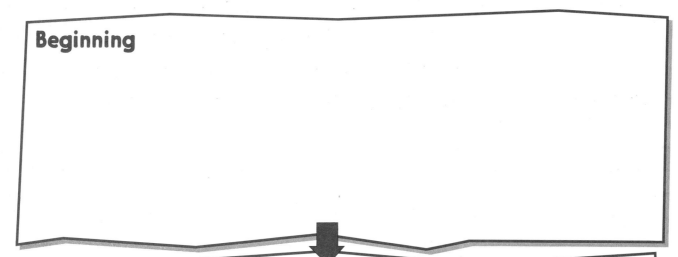

Beginning

Middle

End

voicesreading Grade 3

Name _____

Main Idea Think about the story **One Grain of Rice**. Complete the web using information from the story.

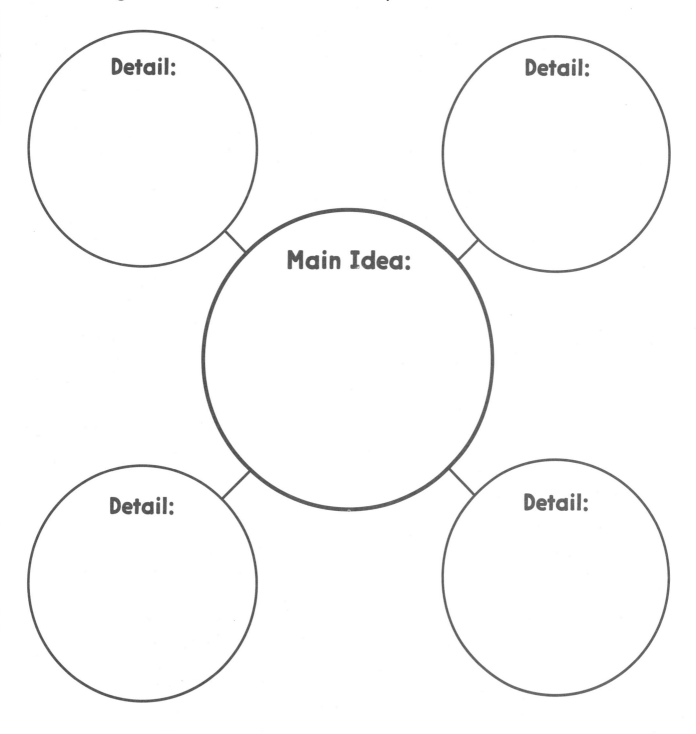

voicesreading Grade 3

Name _____

Words Ending With -er, -est Add **-er** and **-est** to the end of each word in **dark print**. Write the new word in the correct column. (**Hint**: You will have to change the spelling before you add the endings to some words.)

	Add -er	**Add -est**
1. heavy		
2. big		
3. sweet		
4. late		
5. large		
6. hot		
7. sticky		
8. safe		
9. cold		
10. funny		
11. thin		
12. safe		

Copyright © Zaner-Bloser, Inc.

Name _____

Write the vocabulary word from the box that best completes each group of words.

rely	**exotic**	**pure**
balanced	**function**	**nutritious**

1. healthful, good, balanced, _____

2. strange, unusual, different, _____

3. equal, symmetric, square, _____

4. live, perform, work, _____

5. unmixed, simple, perfect, _____

6. depend on, count on, trust in, _____

Now, use each vocabulary word in a complete sentence.

7. _____

8. _____

9. _____

10. _____

11. _____

12. _____

Name _____

Character Sketch A **character sketch** describes a character's personality, looks, likes, and dislikes. Organizing this information helps you write stories.

Think about a character from a story you have read. Answer the questions below about that character.

I. What is the character's name? _____

2. How old is the character? _____

3. Where does the character live? _____

4. What does the character look like? _____

_____

5. Who is in the character's family?_____

_____

6. What hobbies does the character have? _____

_____

7. Who are the character's friends? _____

_____

8. What problems does the character have?_____

_____

Name _____

Words Ending With -ed, -ing Add **-ed** or **-ing** to each word in **dark print** to complete each sentence. Write the new word on the line. (**Hint:** You will have to change the spelling before you add the ending to some words.)

I. I like _____ my toys with my cousin.   **share**

2. We are _____ a trip to visit Aunt Freda.   **take**

3. We _____ for hours to find the perfect gift.   **shop**

4. I like _____ on our frozen pond in the winter.   **skate**

5. We cleaned our garage and _____ the boxes to charity.   **donate**

6. We _____ our hands on brown paper.   **trace**

7. I _____ after I put pepper on my salad.   **sneeze**

8. James was looking up at the sky, _____ at the moon and stars.   **gaze**

9. I can't see anything because I keep _____ my glasses!   **misplace**

10. My uncle _____ the turkey for the Thanksgiving meal.   **carve**

Name _____

Spelling Words

hotter	hottest	larger	largest
later	latest	redder	reddest
sharper	sharpest	wider	widest

Unscramble the letters in **dark print** to make spelling words from the box. Write the words correctly on the lines.

l. **pestshar** _____

2. **widets** _____

3. **tterho** _____

4. **derwi** _____

5. **teddesr** _____

6. **aterl** _____

7. **statel** _____

8. **testhot** _____

9. **garler** _____

10. **perarsh** _____

ll. **gestlar** _____

12. **erredd** _____

voicesreading Grade 3

Copyright © Zaner-Bloser, Inc.

Name _____

Using an Encyclopedia **Encyclopedias** are sets of books that contain information on many topics. The topics are listed alphabetically. Encyclopedias are in the reference section at the library.

Where would you find the following topics? Write the number of the encyclopedia from above next to the topic.

1. recycling _____

2. Niagara Falls _____

3. Dalmatians _____

4. tornadoes _____

5. gems _____

6. penguins _____

7. Ohio River _____

8. Henry Ford _____

9. sunflowers _____

10. windmills _____

Name _____

Base Words and Endings Divide most words into syllables between the base word and the ending.

   Examples: free/dom

   aware/ness

   lump/y

passing	postage	friendly	kindness
washer	thoughtful	kingdom	festive
graceful	bumpy	cruising	lately

Write the words from the box in **ABC order.** Then draw a line between the base words and the endings.

1. _____   2. _____

3. _____   4. _____

5. _____   6. _____

7. _____   8. _____

9. _____   10. _____

11. _____   12. _____

Name _____

Write the vocabulary word from the box that matches each definition.

> cling   possesses   cultivate   informs   exist   moldy

I. tells about   _____

2. covered with fungus   _____

3. has   _____

4. to stick   _____

5. to grow and raise   _____

6. are found in   _____

Write the vocabulary word that best completes each sentence.

7. Baby monkeys often _____ to their mothers.

8. Many types of insects _____ in nature.

9. The newspaper _____ the town about events.

10. Yuck! This old bread is _____!

II. The museum _____ the heaviest diamond.

12. Farmers _____ crops such as corn and wheat.

Name _____

Main Idea Choose the main idea from the box that goes with the supporting details below. Write the main idea on the line.

> There are many ways to get to school.
> There are good reasons to play sports.
> Doctors help people in many ways.
> My dog is the best dog.
> There are many things to do in the summer.

I. **Main Idea:** _____

He fetches the newspaper every morning.
He can catch a ball in midair.
He can push the button on an elevator.
He always barks to let us know someone is at the door.

2. **Main Idea:** _____

They give people medicine.
They operate to help patients get better.
They give shots to prevent sickness.
They work together to keep people healthy.

3. **Main Idea:** _____

You can take the bus.
Some people walk there.
Mom and Dad take me every morning.
Sometimes, people ride their bikes to get there.

voicesreading Grade 3

Copyright © Zaner-Bloser, Inc.

Name _____

Avoiding Using Extra Pronouns Proofread the paragraph.
Cross out any extra pronouns.

My grandma she is a special person. My sister and I we are very lucky to have Grandma in our lives. She never forgets any of my family's our birthdays. She treats them birthdays as if they are the most important days of the year. My dad he said Grandma she was like that when he was a boy. She herself once had a surprise party for him and invited all of his friends. His friends they jumped out from behind the trees in his backyard! Yes, Grandma she is a special person in my family.

Name _____

Identifying Obstacles Think about how you can reach your personal goal. What obstacles or problems do you need to overcome? Complete the sentences below.

voicesreading Grade 3

My Goal: _____

1. The obstacles or problems I need to overcome are _____

   _____

   _____

   _____

2. These obstacles get in the way of achieving my goal by ____

   _____

   _____

   _____

3. One way I can overcome these obstacles is _____

   _____

   _____

   _____

Name _____

Words Ending With -er, -est Circle the word that best completes each sentence.

1. The car ride to Aunt Terri's house was _____ than I remembered.

   long   **longer**   **longest**

2. Maybe our car was just the _____ one on the road.

   slow   **slower**   **slowest**

3. It is so much _____ to fly than it is to drive.

   fast   **faster**   **fastest**

4. My sister is _____ taking long car rides than she is flying in a plane.

   happy   **happier**   **happiest**

5. This year the roads seem _____ than they were last year.

   busy   **busier**   **busiest**

6. Two years ago, we flew on the _____ plane I had ever seen.

   big   **bigger**   **biggest**

7. It was also the _____ plane I had ever heard!

   noisy   **noisier**   **noisiest**

8. The flight attendants were _____ than others I'd met.

   nice   **nicer**   **nicest**

Name _____

Spelling Words

hotter	hottest	larger	largest	later	latest
redder	reddest	sharper	sharpest	wider	widest

Write the spelling words that best complete each group of words.

1. hot, _____, _____

2. late, _____, _____

3. large, _____, _____

4. wide, _____, _____

5. red, _____, _____

6. sharp, _____, _____

Unscramble the letters in **dark print** to make spelling words. Write the words correctly on the lines.

7. **ttoher** _____

8. **taeslt** _____

9. **shpstear** _____

10. **dreder** _____

11. **wride** _____

12. **graler** _____

13. **switde** _____

14. **tserdde** _____

15. **thotste** _____

16. **rlate** _____

17. **gstelar** _____

18. **psharre** _____

Name _____

Inflected Forms Write the base word of the inflected word in **dark print** on the line.

1. We are going to the **fanciest** restaurant in town for dinner. _____

2. The dog **buried** another bone in the backyard. _____

3. This movie was **scarier** than the one I saw last night. _____

4. We **caught** several fish yesterday at the lake. _____

5. I **forgot** to make my bed this morning. _____

6. The ice cream **melted** all over the counter. _____

7. My cousin has the **prettiest** garden in her neighborhood. _____

8. I **stubbed** my toe because the sidewalk was uneven. _____

9. The green bug **crept** across the kitchen table. _____

10. The cat is **pouncing** on a little rubber ball. _____

voicesreading Grade 3

Name _____

Circle the vocabulary word that best completes each sentence.

1. I would love to visit an _____ place that I've never been to before.

   exotic   **flawless**   **insistent**   **nutritious**

2. It is important to eat a _____ diet and get plenty of rest.

   exotic   **slight**   **balanced**   **rowdy**

3. _____ food helps keep us healthy.

   Silky   **Nutritious**   **Tired**   **Plush**

4. It is hard to _____ when you are tired.

   function   **book**   **team up**   **give away**

5. Drinking _____ water is a healthful thing you can do.

   poor   **function**   **pure**   **blissful**

6. We _____ on the bus to get us to work and to school.

   function   **rely**   **float**   **haul**

Name _____

Use the vocabulary words from the box to complete the paragraph. Write the words on the lines.

cling	**possesses**	**cultivate**
informs	**exist**	**moldy**

Do best friends still _____? Yes! Let me tell you

about my friend Lea. She _____ good qualities such

as kindness and loyalty. When she notices that someone is being

teased, she _____ the bully that teasing is wrong.

One time at lunch, she noticed that the bread on my sandwich

was _____. What did she do? She shared her

lunch with me! When she grows up she wants to help

_____ food so no one goes hungry.

Now you can see why people

_____ to Lea. She's a

great person!

voicesreading Grade 3

Theme 5: Love and Friendship 149

Name _____

Author's Viewpoint Answer the questions about the story **One Grain of Rice**. Write your answers on the lines.

I. What does the author think about the raja? _____

_____

_____

2. What does the author think about Rani? _____

_____

_____

3. What does the author think about greed? _____

_____

_____

4. Why does the author think a raja should be wise and fair?

_____

_____

_____

voicesreading Grade 3

Name _____

Text Structure: Character and Setting Think about the story **The Babe and I**. Complete the webs with information from the story.

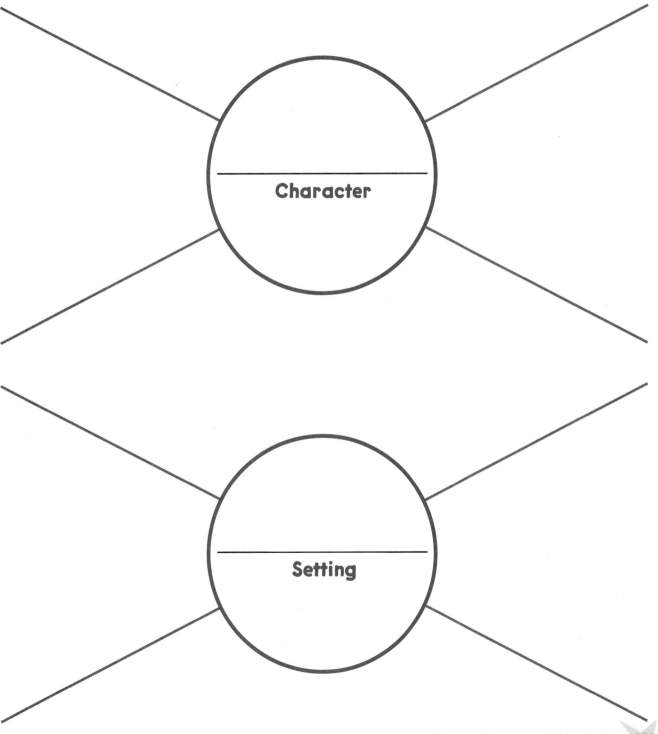

Character

Setting

Name _____

Words Ending With -le Write a word with **-le** that names each picture.

1.  _____

2.  _____

3. 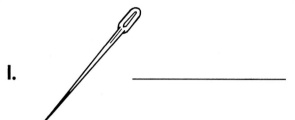 _____

4. 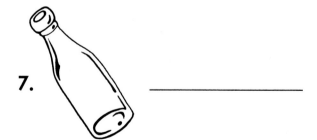 _____

5.  _____

6. 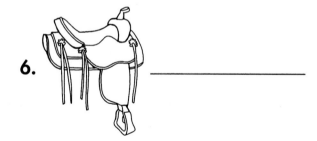 _____

7. 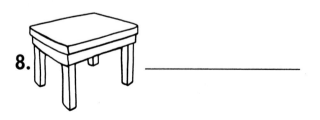 _____

8. 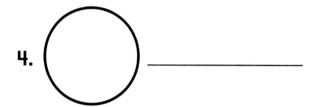 _____

9. 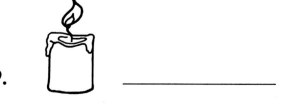 _____

10.

Name _____

Draw a line to match each vocabulary word in **dark print** with its definition.

l. **recited**   poor

2. **victorious**   very hot

3. **needy**   put up with difficulties

4. **refund**   said from memory

5. **suffered**   being the winner

6. **scorching**   money paid back for something

Now, use each vocabulary word in a complete sentence. Write the sentences on the lines.

7. _____

8. _____

9. _____

10. _____

ll. _____

l2. _____

Name _____

> **Sentence Elaboration** When you write a paper, reread it to yourself. Does anything seem unclear? If so, you may need to **elaborate**. **Elaborate** means to **expand** or give more information.
>
> Example: (original) There was a bird.
> (more details) There was a red bird chirping outside my window.

Read the sentences. Elaborate to give more information.
(**Hint:** The question(s) at the end of each sentence will help you elaborate.)

1. I hope my friend visits today. (**Why?**)

_____

2. She said something that wasn't nice. (**What?**)

_____

3. I saw him. (**Who? Where?**)

_____

4. He is so fun. (**Who? Why?**)

_____

5. I will never forget my last birthday. (**Why?**)

_____

6. Hawaii is my favorite place to visit. (**Why?**)

_____

voicesreading Grade 3

Copyright © Zaner-Bloser, Inc.

Name _____

Words Ending With -er, -est Write the word from the box that best completes each sentence.

colder	taller	softer	bluer	scarier
coldest	tallest	softest	bluest	scariest

I. I am _____ than my brother, but my dad is the

_____ person in the family.

2. My eyes are _____ than my mom's eyes, but

my brother's eyes are the _____ of all.

3. Ebony's pillow is _____ than Kai's, but Mika's

pillow is the _____ pillow in the house.

4. I saw the _____ movie I've ever seen last night.

It was even _____ than I thought it would be.

5. Yesterday was the _____day of the year. It was

_____ than last Wednesday.

Name _____

Spelling Words

ladle	puzzle	table	beetle	castle	maple
bubble	riddle	cattle	nibble	cradle	rattle

Write the spelling words in **ABC order**. Then draw a line to separate the syllables.

1. _____

2. _____

3. _____

4. _____

5. _____

6. _____

7. _____

8. _____

9. _____

10. _____

11. _____

12. _____

voicesreading Grade 3

Copyright © Zaner-Bloser, Inc.

Name _____

Evaluating Sources When choosing sources for information, ask yourself the following questions:

- **Does the source provide the facts?**
- **Does the source offer enough information?**
- **Is the information objective?**
- **Is the information up-to-date?**
- **Is the source reliable?**

Imagine that you are writing a paragraph about whales. Read about the different sources you may find at the library. Put a ✔ in the box next to the best sources.

☐ **1. Whales, Whales, and More Whales** is a book about whales written by a marine biologist. (A marine biologist is a scientist who studies animals that live in the water.)

☐ **2.** *Whale Times* is a magazine written by people who work with whales.

☐ **3.** "Why I Like Whales" is an article written by a student in the third grade.

☐ **4. 10 Facts About Whales** is a video that tells how whales eat, sleep, and breathe.

☐ **5. Willy the Whale** is a book about a boy who has a pet whale.

Name _____

Words With -le Divide words that end with **-le** before the consonant that is before the **-le**.

Examples: ta/ble
us/a/ble
syl/la/ble

Write the words in the box below in **ABC order**. Then, draw a line to divide the syllables.

> terrible   wrinkle   noble   horrible   vehicle   uncle
> rattle   struggle   maple   mantle   crinkle   incredible

1. _____   2. _____

3. _____   4. _____

5. _____   6. _____

7. _____   8. _____

9. _____   10. _____

11. _____   12. _____

voicesreading Grade 3

Copyright © Zaner-Bloser, Inc.

Name _____

Unscramble the letters in **dark print** to spell the vocabulary word that matches each definition. Write the word correctly on the lines.

wages	**greedy**	**patrolled**
brace	**barely**	**loaned**

1. **ptllderoa**   moved about an area, while watching or guarding it   __ __ ◯ __ __ __ __ __ __

2. **gawse**   pay for work   __ __ __ __ ◯

3. **acrbe**   to hold oneself up   __ __ __ ◯ __

4. **reably**   almost not; hardly   __ __ __ ◯ __ __

5. **eedrgy**   desiring more than one needs   __ __ __ __ __ __

6. **neaold**   allowed to borrow   __ __ __ ◯ __ __

Write the circled letters from above on the lines below.

__ __ __ __ __

Now, unscramble the letters to answer the riddle.

What did the penny say to its friend?

"We make perfect ___ ___ ___ ___ ___!"

Name _____

Text Structure: Character and Setting Think about the story
The Babe and I to answer these questions.

I. Where did the boy in the story sell his newspapers?

_____

2. Why did he choose that location?

_____

_____

3. Who was Babe Ruth?

_____

4. Whom did the boy feel sympathy for in the story? Why?

_____

_____

5. Where did the boy's father work?

_____

6. Why was everyone struggling during this time?

_____

Name _____

Making Forms of be Agree Use the word **am, is, are, was,** or **were** to complete each sentence.

1. We _____ late because our car had a flat tire.

2. I _____ sure I will have a good time visiting the museum.

3. My friend _____ going to a horse show this weekend.

4. I _____ hoping we could go to the museum tomorrow.

5. My parents _____ taking a trip to Alaska next summer.

6. When _____ you going to make your bed?

7. I _____ helping my neighbor rake the leaves last night.

8. He _____ getting good grades in all of his classes.

9. My grandparents _____ out of town for two weeks.

10. I _____ knitting a hat for each person in my family.

Name _____

My Personal Plan What are the steps that will lead you to your goal? Try to think about three things that you will have to do to achieve your goal.

voicesreading Grade 3

My Goal: _____

I. The obstacles I have to overcome are _____

_____

_____ .

2. Three steps I will take to overcome these obstacles are

_____

_____

_____

_____

_____ .

Name _____

Words Ending With -le Write a word from the box to match each clue.

little	fiddle	battle	whistle	vehicle
kettle	apple	rattle	cattle	castle

1. This is an instrument that looks like a violin. _____

2. This is the opposite of **big**. _____

3. This could be used at a basketball game. _____

4. This is a container for boiling water. _____

5. A baby may play with this. _____

6. These are cows, bulls, or oxen. _____

7. This is another word for **fight**. _____

8. This is a very large house. _____

9. This red object is a type of fruit. _____

10. A car or truck is this. _____

Name _____

Circle the misspelled words and write them correctly on the lines below.

A large bubbule formed in the mayple syrup after Mom plopped the lattle in it. I ate my pancakes and watched Dad nybble on his food while he worked on a puzlle. A little beetell scurried across the floor and hid under the fridge.

"I have a ridle for everyone. 'What is round, shiny, and worn in a kastle?'" asked Dad.

Mom answered, "I'm not sure," as she moved my baby brother's craydle next to the tayble. "Do you know?" she asked my brother. He just shook his raddle and cooed.

Then Dad stood up and said, "Oh well. I have to take care of the cattell. I will finish this later."

I thought for a moment. Then it came to me.

"A crown! A crown is shiny, and worn in a castle!" I shouted.

I. _____   2. _____

3. _____   4. _____

5. _____   6. _____

7. _____   8. _____

9. _____   10. _____

II. _____   12. _____

Name _____

Base Words and Endings Rewrite each word in **dark print** and divide it between the base word and the ending. Then write the base word. (**Hint:** You will have to change the spelling for some base words.)

1. **peaceful** _____ _____

2. **gentleness** _____ _____

3. **politeness** _____ _____

4. **happiness** _____ _____

5. **joyous** _____ _____

6. **hopeful** _____ _____

7. **bluest** _____ _____

8. **truthful** _____ _____

9. **forgiveness** _____ _____

10. **excitement** _____ _____

11. **suddenly** _____ _____

12. **closest** _____ _____

13. **timely** _____ _____

14. **friendly** _____ _____

Name _____

Choose the vocabulary word from the box to replace the word or words in **dark print** in each sentence. Write the word on the line.

> scorching   suffered   refund
> needy   recited   victorious

I. Destiny was **being the winner** in the science contest. _____

2. Luther and his family **put up with difficulties** when his mother lost her job. _____

3. There are many people in the world who are **poor**. _____

4. We had to practice soccer today under the **very hot** midday sun. _____

5. He **said from memory** the speech in front of the entire class. _____

6. This money is a **pay back** for the pants I returned to the store. _____

voicesreading Grade 3

Name _____

Write the vocabulary word from the box that best completes each sentence.

wages	**greedy**	**patrolled**
brace	**barely**	**loaned**

I. I think my brother was being _____ when he ate all of the bread Mom baked.

2. My friend _____ me her jacket, but now I can't find it anywhere.

3. India _____ passed the test because she did not study very hard.

4. José had to _____ himself to keep from falling when the ride came to a stop.

5. The dog that _____ the factory made it impossible for a thief to break in.

6. Our company paid us our _____ at the end of each week.

Name _____

Main Idea Think about the story **The Babe and I**. Complete the chart below.

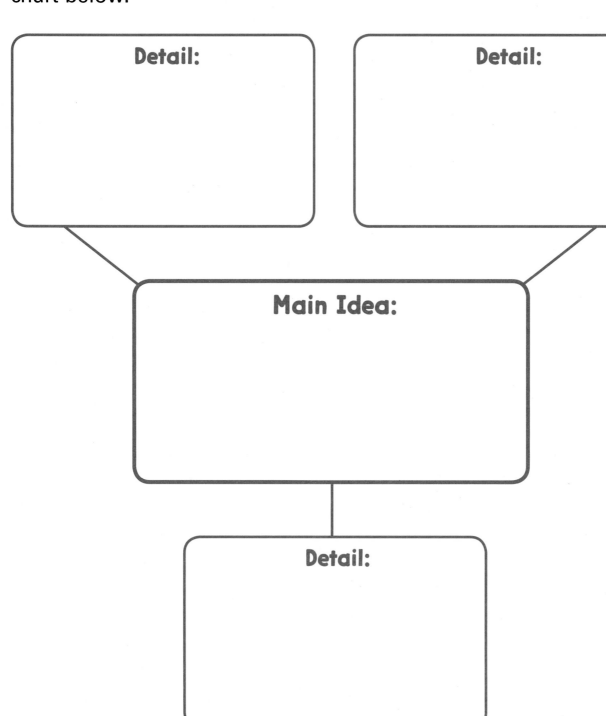

Detail:

Detail:

Main Idea:

Detail:

Name _____

Noting Details Think about the story **Candy Shop**. Choose one of the topics in the box and write it in the small circle. Then write details about the topic from the story in the large circles.

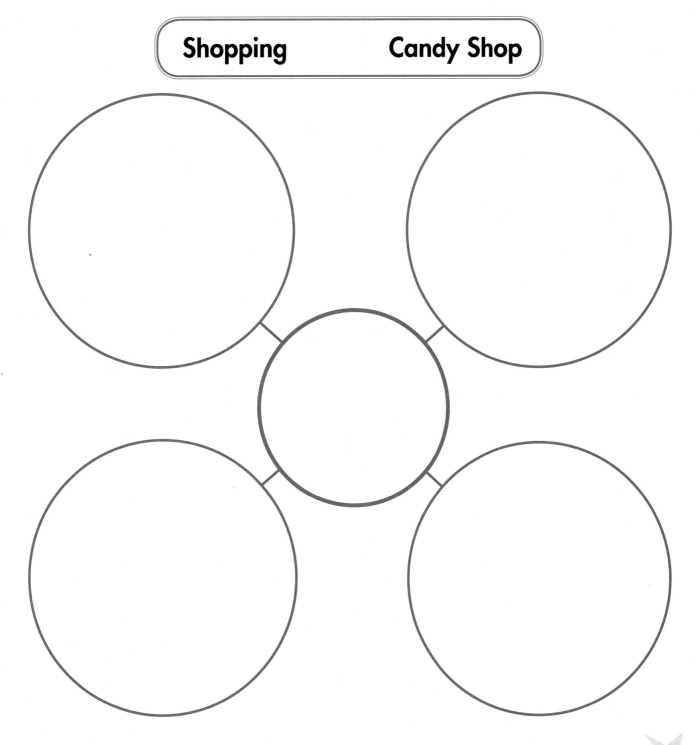

Shopping   Candy Shop

voicesreading Grade 3

Name _____

Silent Consonants kn, mb, wr, gn Look at the pictures. Write the missing letters from the box to name the pictures.

| kn | mb | wr | gn |

1. co_____

2. _____ot

3. _____ap

4. _____aw

5. _____ite

6. _____ee

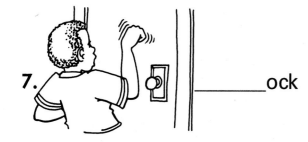

7. _____ock

8. la_____

Name _____

Complete the crossword puzzle with the vocabulary words from the box.

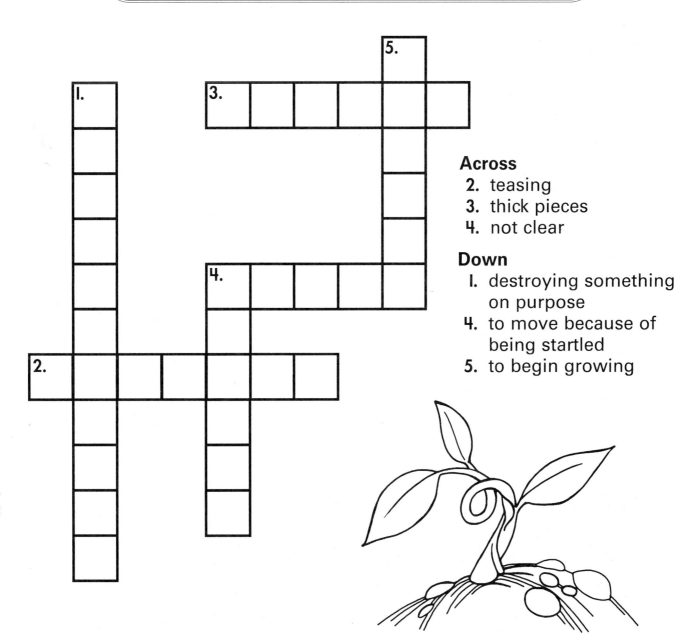

| sprout | flinch | vandalizing |
| clumps | faint | kidding |

Across
2. teasing
3. thick pieces
4. not clear

Down
1. destroying something on purpose
4. to move because of being startled
5. to begin growing

Name _____

Stating Fact and Opinion Read each sentence. Write **F** on the line if it is a **fact**. Write **O** on the line if it is an **opinion**.

1. Whales often spend the winter off the shores of Maui. _____

2. Whales need more environmental protection. _____

3. Science is the most interesting subject in school. _____

4. Astronomers are scientists who study the stars and planets. _____

5. Dogs are the best pets to have. _____

6. Recycling is a waste of time. _____

7. The *Mona Lisa* is a famous painting. _____

8. Poems should always have rhyming lines. _____

Write a **fact** about reading. _____

_____

Write an **opinion** about reading. _____

_____

voicesreading Grade 3

Copyright © Zaner-Bloser, Inc.

voicesreading Grade 3

Name _____

Word Ending With -le Read the words in the box. Write each word in the correct column. One word will be used twice.

noble	ankle	settle	castle	purple	wiggle
vehicle	giggle	gentle	jungle	struggle	little

Nouns	Verbs	Adjectives
_____	_____	_____
_____	_____	_____
_____	_____	_____
_____	_____	_____
_____		

Choose one word from each column. Use each word in a complete sentence.

1. _____

   _____

2. _____

   _____

3. _____

   _____

Name _____

Unscramble the letters in **dark print**. Draw a line to the spelling word in the right column that matches.

I. **brumc**   climb

2. **ngaw**   comb

3. **nkeads**   crumb

4. **nifek**   gnat

5. **tonk**   gnaw

6. **stwir**   knew

7. **nownk**   kneads

8. **limcb**   knife

9. **bomc**   kneel

10. **tang**   knot

II. **leenk**   known

12. **newk**   wrist

Name _____

Following Directions Answer the questions about the directions and the map. Write your answers on the lines.

Take Reading Road south for 5 miles to Card Catalog Avenue.
Go east on Card Catalog Avenue for 2 miles.
Go south on Reference Row.
Go to first driveway on the left.
Turn in the first driveway.

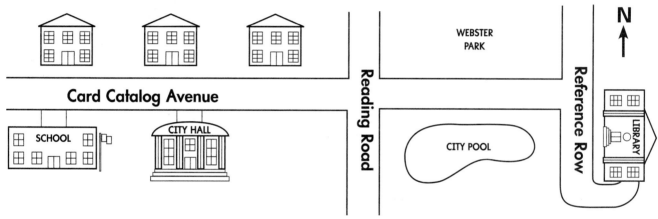

1. Which direction do you go on Reference Row?

   _____

2. Which direction do you go on Card Catalog Avenue?

   _____

3. How many miles do you go on Reading Road?

   _____

4. Which way do you turn in the driveway?

   _____

5. About how many miles will you travel to get to your destination?

   _____

6. Where do these directions take you?

   _____

Name _____

Persuasive Read this example of a speech explaining why we should welcome newcomers to the United States.

voicesreading Grade 3

There are many reasons we should welcome new people to the United States. First, kindness helps newcomers feel welcome. Many people are scared to move to a different place. Second, people that come here bring their cultures with them. They can teach others about where they came from. We can learn about places we've never visited! Lastly, it's important to welcome newcomers because that is what this country is all about! The United States is a place for people from all over the world. I believe we should welcome newcomers because they make the United States more interesting.

Name _____

> **Prefixes re- and un-** The prefix **re-** means "again" or "back."
>
> **Example: redo** means "do again"
>
> The prefix **un-** means "not" or "opposite of."
>
> **Example: unpack** means "the opposite of pack"

Add the prefix **re-** or **un-** to each word in **dark print** to make a word that matches the clue. Write the new word on the line.

I. the opposite of **lock**   _____

2. to **tell** again   _____

3. the opposite of **load**   _____

4. not **fair**   _____

5. not **lucky**   _____

6. to **play** again   _____

7. not **happy**   _____

8. the opposite of **do**   _____

9. to **appear** again   _____

10. not **interesting**   _____

II. to **write** again   _____

12. to **elect** again   _____

Name _____

Write the vocabulary word from the box that best completes each group of words.

strength	**stakes**	**commanded**
dingy	**stark**	**shifted**

1. harsh, intense, jarring, _____

2. moved, traveled, changed, _____

3. posts, stamps, markers, _____

4. power, support, toughness, _____

5. grimy, filthy, dirty, _____

6. told, demanded, ordered, _____

Now, use each vocabulary word in a complete sentence.

7. _____

8. _____

9. _____

10. _____

11. _____

12. _____

voicesreading Grade 3

Name _____

Noting Details Answer the questions about the story **Candy Shop**. Write the answers on the lines.

l. What is the boy in the story pretending to be? _____

_____

2. What is the difference between Aunt Thelma's street and the streets they walk along on their way to go shopping?

_____

_____

3. Why are people gathered in front of the Candy Shop?

_____

_____

4. Why does Miz Chu look scared? _____

_____

5. What does Aunt Thelma think most people are like?

_____

_____

6. Why does the boy clean the sidewalk? _____

_____

Name _____

Possessive Pronouns Write the pronoun from the box that best completes each sentence.

> **My   Your   His   Her   Its   Their   Our**

1. I live on College Street. _____ apartment is in the building on the hill.

2. Ben is an excellent hockey player. _____ team won the state championship last year.

3. My neighbors have two big dogs. _____ dogs' names are Fluffy and Juma.

4. My family likes to play games on the weekends. _____ favorite game is checkers.

5. Jordan loves all kinds of animals. _____ dream is to be a veterinarian someday.

6. You have a great personality. _____ smile makes everyone feel happy.

7. That flower is beautiful. _____ petals are a unique shade of pink.

8. I have three good friends. _____ friends are Kate, Latisha, and Miko.

9. José goes to Mexico every year. _____ grandma and grandpa live there.

10. This bike is very colorful. _____ handles are blue, and its wheels are yellow.

voicesreading Grade 3

Copyright © Zaner-Bloser, Inc.

Name _____

Order-of-Importance Chart You can use an Order-of-Importance Chart to organize ideas for your speech.

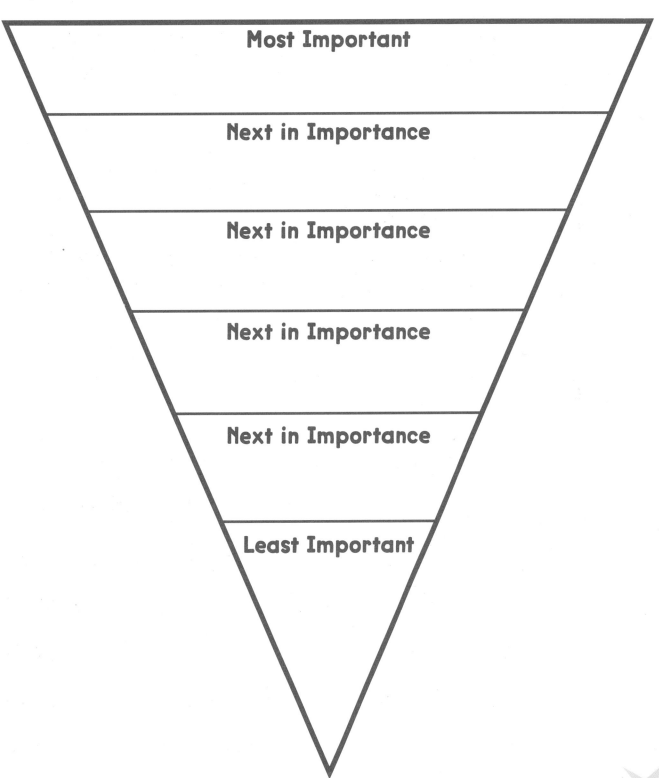

Most Important

Next in Importance

Next in Importance

Next in Importance

Next in Importance

Least Important

Name _____

What Do I Need to Achieve My Goal? Think about the things the characters in the stories needed to achieve their dreams and goals. Then complete the sentences below about your personal goal.

My Goal: _____

1. Three values I need to achieve this goal are _____

_____

because _____

_____

_____

_____.

2. Three skills I need to achieve this goal are

_____

because _____

_____

_____

_____.

voicesreading Grade 3

Name _____

Silent Consonants kn, mb, wr, gn Choose the consonant pair from the box to complete each word. Write the letters on the lines.

kn	gn	mb	wr

I. My fingers were nu_____ after I'd been playing in the snow all day.

2. A _____at was flying around the trash.

3. Please _____ock before you open the door.

4. I like to _____ap birthday gifts.

5. My face _____inkles when I smile.

6. My dog likes to _____aw on bones.

7. I _____ew all of the answers to the questions on the test.

8. I fell off my bike and broke my _____ist.

9. My baby sister sucks her thu_____ when she's tired.

10. My aunt knows how to _____it scarves.

Name _____

Spelling Words

climb	comb	crumb	gnat	gnaw	kneads
kneel	knife	knot	know	known	wrist

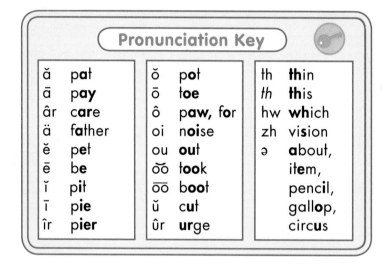

Pronunciation Key

ă	pat	ŏ	pot	th	thin
ā	pay	ō	toe	th	this
âr	care	ô	paw, for	hw	which
ä	father	oi	noise	zh	vision
ĕ	pet	ou	out	ə	about,
ē	be	ŏŏ	took		item,
ĭ	pit	ōō	boot		pencil,
ī	pie	ŭ	cut		gallop,
îr	pier	ûr	urge		circus

Write the spelling word from the box that matches each respelling. Use the pronunciation key to help you.

1. /rĭst/ _____

2. /nēdz/ _____

3. /năt/ _____

4. /nōn/ _____

5. /nô/ _____

6. /kōm/ _____

7. /nō/ _____

8. /nŏt/ _____

9. /klīm/ _____

10. /nēl/ _____

11. /nīf/ _____

12. /krŭm/ _____

Name _____

Words With -le Write a word with **-le** that names each picture. Draw a line between the syllables.

1. _____

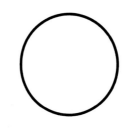

2. _____

3. _____

4. _____

5. _____

6. _____

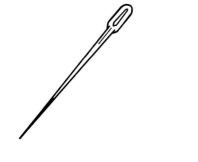

7. _____

8. _____

Name _____

Use this checklist when you revise your writing.

Revising Checklist: Persuasive

yes	no	Is the opinion stated in the first paragraph and mentioned again in the last paragraph?
yes	no	Is a summary of reasons for the opinion in the first paragraph?
yes	no	Does the speech have many details and facts to give a strong argument?
yes	no	Do facts and examples support the opinions?
yes	no	Is each reason listed in the order of importance?
yes	no	Do all details, examples, and reasons support the main topic?
yes	no	Does every sentence begin with a capital letter and end with the correct punctuation?
yes	no	Are the possessive pronouns used correctly?

voicesreading Grade 3

Copyright © Zaner-Bloser, Inc.

Name _____

Circle the vocabulary word that best completes each sentence.

I. We are excited when the flowers begin to _____ in the spring.

clump   **sprout**   **scowl**   **trudge**

2. The scar on my leg from my bike accident has grown _____ over the years.

faint   **flinch**   **pure**   **vexed**

3. _____ other people's things is against the law.

Kidding   **Peering**   **Shuffling**   **Vandalizing**

4. It is difficult not to _____ when my sister sneaks behind me and says, "Boo!"

sprout   **overhear**   **flinch**   **rely**

5. I was just _____ with you. I did not mean to hurt your feelings.

vandalizing   **kidding**   **victorious**   **smirking**

6. The mashed potatoes were delicious, even though they had _____ in them.

clumps   **faint**   **tugs**   **wardrobes**

voicesreading Grade 3

Name _____

Write the vocabulary words from the box that best complete the paragraph.

strength	**stakes**	**commanded**
dingy	**stark**	**shifted**

Last year, my family volunteered to live on the

_____ planet Mars for a month. We had to rely

on our _____ to meet the challenges of living in

another place. We built our home out of the spaceship we used

to get there. It was very small and always _____

from the dust outside. Mom and Dad _____ that

we clean every night, but we could never get rid of all of the dirt.

Then, some other settlers placed _____ between

our homes. The stakes helped us find our

way during dust storms. Over time,

the dust _____ and buried

our markers. Luckily, no one ever got lost. Life on

Mars was hard, but it was also a great adventure.

voicesreading Grade 3

Name _____

Text Structure: Character and Setting Think about the story **Candy Shop**. Complete the chart with information from the story.

Characters	Setting(s)
1.	
2.	
3.	

Write one sentence about each character. Write what the character might have said about what happened at the Candy Shop.

1. _____

2. _____

3. _____

voicesreading Grade 3

Name _____

Problem and Solution Think about the story **The Streets Are Free**. Complete the chart with information from the story.

Problem: The children need a place to play.		
Solutions	**Pros**	**Cons**
1.		
2.		
3.		

voicesreading Grade 3

Copyright © Zaner-Bloser, Inc.

Name _____

Vowel Teams oi, oy Write the word with **oi** or **oy** that names each picture.

1. _____   2. _____

3. _____   4. _____

5. _____   6. _____

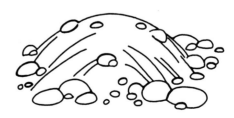

7. _____   8. _____

Name _____

Write the vocabulary word from the box that matches each definition.

voicesreading Grade 3

| diverse | wends | irrigation |
| milestone | critically | captivity |

1. an important event   _____

2. in a state of crisis or emergency   _____

3. the act of bringing water to dry land   _____

4. moves along a course or route   _____

5. having different qualities or aspects   _____

6. the condition of being confined   _____

Now, use each vocabulary word in a complete sentence.

7. _____

8. _____

9. _____

10. _____

11. _____

12. _____

Name _____

Audience Your readers are your **audience**. Are you writing for other students in your class? Are you writing for a special person? Once you know who your audience is, think about what that audience needs to know.

Make a list of three topics for your speech.

Topic 1: _____

Topic 2: _____

Topic 3: _____

Who is your audience for each topic?

Audience: _____

Audience: _____

Audience: _____

Now, choose one topic and an audience for your speech. Write the topic and the audience on the lines below.

The topic I choose is _____ .

The audience I choose is _____ .

Name _____

Write the word from the box that names each picture.

wrench	**knob**	**crumbs**	**write**	**wrinkle**
climb	**gnome**	**wreck**	**thumb**	**knock**

voicesreading Grade 3

 1. _____

 2. _____

 3. _____

4. _____

 5. _____

 6. _____

 7. _____

 8. _____

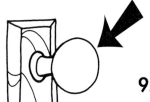 9. _____

 10. _____

Name _____

Spelling Words

enjoy	foil	join	joy	loyal	moist
oyster	point	soil	toil	voice	voyage

Unscramble the letters in **dark print** to make spelling words from the box. Write the words correctly on the lines.

1. **ageyov** _____

2. **loit** _____

3. **topin** _____

4. **stoim** _____

5. **oyj** _____

6. **lifo** _____

7. **joyen** _____

8. **noji** _____

9. **alloy** _____

10. **steryo** _____

11. **liso** _____

12. **cevoi** _____

Name _____

> **Know Your Strengths and Weaknesses** **Strengths** are things people do well. **Weaknesses** are things people need help doing or need to improve.
>
> **Examples:** Michelle is good at drawing pictures. (Drawing is her **strength**.)
>
> Ben needs help reading music. (Reading music is his **weakness**.)

Think about your strengths and weaknesses as you complete the sentences below.

1. One strength I have is _____ .

2. One way I can use this strength is _____

_____

_____ .

3. One weakness I have is _____

_____

_____ .

4. One way I can improve this weakness is _____

_____

_____ .

voicesreading Grade 3

Name _____

> **Suffixes -ly and -ful** The suffix **-ly** means "like" or "in the manner of." The suffix **-ful** means "full of."
>
> **Examples:** **sisterly** means "like a sister"
>
> **hopeful** means "full of hope"

Read the clues. Add the suffix **-ly** or **-ful** to each word in **dark print** to make a word that matches each definition. Write the new word on the line.

1. full of **cheer** _____

2. done in a **quick** way _____

3. full of **wonder** _____

4. full of **thanks** _____

5. done in a **nice** way _____

6. done in a **happy** way _____

7. like a **father** _____

8. full of **care** _____

9. like a **friend** _____

10. done in a **cheerful** way _____

11. full of **fear** _____

12. full of **truth** _____

Name _____

Draw a line to match each vocabulary word in **dark print** with its definition.

l. **gradual**

an amount of land that is set aside for a specific purpose

2. **rugged**

slow; step-by-step

3. **contemporary**

tough

4. **anthem**

living in

5. **inhabiting**

an official song about a country

6. **reserve**

modern

Name _____

Problem and Solution   Answer the questions about the story **The Streets Are Free**. Write the answers on the lines.

I. What is the problem in the story?

_____

_____

2. Why is it a problem?

_____

_____

3. How did the problem start?

_____

_____

4. How does the community solve the problem?

_____

_____

5. What other solution to the problem can you think of?

_____

_____

Name _____

Adverbs Choose the adverb from the box that best completes each sentence.

| carefully | quietly | foolishly | gently | repeatedly |
| loudly | sleepily | hungrily | slowly | quickly |

1. I crept down the stairs _____ so I wouldn't wake my family.

2. The dog barked _____ and scared the rabbits.

3. The mother _____ rocked the baby to sleep.

4. He _____ ate all of the pancakes on his plate.

5. A.J. _____ ran home because he didn't want to be late for dinner.

6. The turtle _____ walked toward the pond.

7. I _____ rubbed my eyes when I woke up.

8. I _____ called my dog, but she never came home.

9. My mother and I _____ crossed the busy street.

10. Melissa _____ waited until the last minute to study for the test.

voicesreading Grade 3

Copyright © Zaner-Bloser, Inc.

Name _____

Achieving My Goal Think about the stories you have read and the people who helped the characters achieve goals. Who can help you achieve your dreams or goals? Work with your partner to complete the sentences below.

My Goal: _____

1. My partner can help me achieve my goal by _____

_____

_____ .

2. Another person who can help me reach my goal is

_____ .

3. This person can help me reach my goal by _____

_____ .

4. Another person who can help is _____

_____ .

5. This person can also help me by _____

_____ .

Name _____

Vowel Teams oi, oy Circle the word that best completes each sentence.

I. The _____ on the heater were rusty and old.

    coy   **coils**   **could**   **coins**

2. The tooth fairy left three _____ under my pillow.

    coins   **coils**   **crows**   **cows**

3. I _____ coloring, painting, and drawing in my notebook.

    noise   **ploy**   **enjoy**   **anno**

4. You have three _____ for lunch: sandwich, soup, or salad.

    poisons   **clouds**   **chooses**   **choices**

5. The _____ from the nearby traffic ruined our camping trip.

    noise   **annoy**   **moist**   **voice**

6. Mrs. Swenson asked me to _____ to my favorite toy.

    voice   **noise**   **poison**   **point**

7. The workers had to _____ the old building because it was not safe.

    broil   **royal**   **destroy**   **enjoy**

8. Mosquitoes _____ me in the summer.

    annoy   **boy**   **loyal**   **royal**

voicesreading Grade 3

Copyright © Zaner-Bloser, Inc.

Name _____

Circle the misspelled words in each sentence. Write the spelling words correctly on the lines.

I. Lacy ate the oystere and said, "Delicious," in a loud voyce.

_____   _____

2. Jordan is willing to toyal on the ship for a chance to take a voiage across the ocean.

_____   _____

3. If you joyn the club, you may injoy the swimming pool anytime.

_____   _____

4. We trained our dog to poynt with his nose when he sees something in the soyal.

_____   _____

5. He takes great joye in his ability to foel my plans.

_____   _____

6. The loyell dog gave her owner a moyst kiss.

_____   _____

Name _____

Prefixes re- and un- Add the prefix **re-** or **un-** to each word from the box to make a word that completes each sentence. Write the new word on the line.

read	fair	happy	take
load	lock	tell	wrap

I. The young child looked very _____ when her balloon popped.

2. I like to _____ gifts on my birthday.

3. My sister asks me to _____ the same books many times.

4. I will help you _____ the suitcases from the car.

5. The photographer is going to _____ our family's picture.

6. My grandpa likes to _____ funny stories about his younger days.

7. Will you please _____ the door for me?

8. It was _____ that my brother won all of the prizes!

voicesreading Grade 3

Name _____

Write the vocabulary word from the box that best completes
each sentence.

diverse	wends	irrigation
milestone	critically	captivity

1. People come here from all over the world, which makes our

   country _____.

2. We can grow almost anything in the desert by using

   _____.

3. My first day of school was an important _____

   in my life.

4. The cyclist _____ her way along the challenging

   race route.

5. He was _____ ill and needed an operation to

   save his life.

6. Some animals are born in _____, not in the wild.

Name _____

Circle the vocabulary word that best completes each sentence.

I. They played the national _____ for the Olympic winners.

anthem   **contemporary**   **corridor**   **milestone**

2. The turtles _____ the island are famous for their interesting behavior.

reserve   **inhabiting**   **shuffling**   **shifted**

3. Learning to play the piano well is a _____ process.

inhabiting   **gradual**   **reserve**   **kidding**

4 The government set aside some land for an animal _____.

rugged   **diverse**   **reserve**   **unrest**

5. Use these sturdy boots to hike over the _____ terrain.

inhabiting   **critically**   **flawless**   **rugged**

6. The new building has a very _____ look.

shifted   **gradual**   **contemporary**   **moldy**

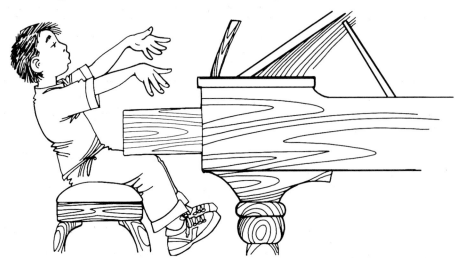

voicesreading Grade 3

Copyright © Zaner-Bloser, Inc.

Name _____

Noting Details Use details to answer the questions about the story **The Streets Are Free**. Write the answers on the lines.

I. What does the mountainside look like where Cheo, Carlitos, and Camila live?

_____

2. Where do the children spend their time after school?

_____

3. Who helps the children plan the details for their banner?

_____

4. Why can't the children see the mayor?

_____

_____

5. Who is interested in what the children have to say?

_____

6. What are some of the things the children want to have on their playground?

_____

_____

Name _____

Text-to-Text Connections Think about the stories **Secret Signs** and **One Grain of Rice**. In both stories, the main characters did things that required them to be brave and clever. Write a paragraph comparing Luke and Rani.

_____

_____

_____

_____

_____

_____

_____

_____

_____

_____

_____

voicesreading Grade 3

Name _____

Long o Spelled oa, oe Circle the word that names each picture.

1.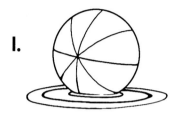

   flew
   foam
   float
   flown

2.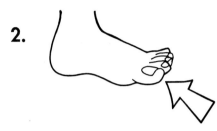

   tow
   toe
   toad
   to

3.

   toast
   toes
   tows
   towels

4.

   throw
   trout
   throat
   toot

5.

   rows
   roast
   roust
   rose

6.

   tows
   toast
   toad
   towed

7.

   goat
   goal
   gown
   goes

8.

   boast
   bows
   boot
   boat

9.

   couch
   crows
   coach
   crutch

10.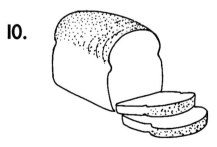

    loaf
    loud
    low
    lose

Name _____

Write the vocabulary words from the box that match the definitions. Write the words on the lines.

| hollow | navigate | smothered |
| ranchers | available | tips |

1. useful information _____

2. covered with a thick layer _____

3. able to be used _____

4. to find the way through something _____

5. to carve out the inside of something _____

6. people who own large farms _____

Now, use each vocabulary word in a complete sentence.

7. _____

8. _____

9. _____

10. _____

11. _____

12. _____

Name _____

Vowel Teams oi, oy Write the word from the box that best completes each sentence.

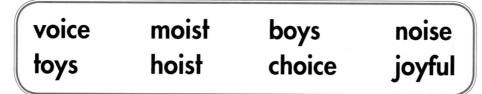

| voice | moist | boys | noise |
| toys | hoist | choice | joyful |

I. My birthday cake was _____ and tasty.

2. The best _____ for a snack is something healthful, such as raisins or yogurt.

3. I am going to donate some of my _____ to the shelter.

4. A loud _____ woke me up this morning.

5. There are many more _____ than there are girls in my class.

6. It was a _____ day when my dad came home from his business trip.

7. I have to _____ the flag every morning before school begins.

8. My _____ is hoarse and scratchy because I am sick.

Name _____

Spelling Words

coast	float	foam	hoe	moan	roast
soak	soap	throat	toad	toast	toe

Circle the hidden spelling words.

```
G  H  O  K  T  O  E  F  J  O
M  O  A  N  J  A  M  L  X  D
U  E  B  E  L  T  S  O  L  G
P  R  O  A  S  T  H  A  M  P
O  H  D  A  W  C  X  T  H  Q
G  O  O  U  S  O  B  F  D  S
B  T  O  S  A  A  S  F  I  T
Y  H  O  O  S  S  T  O  D  B
F  R  J  A  P  T  O  A  U  A
R  O  L  P  O  Z  A  M  I  P
V  A  H  L  R  A  D  W  A  Y
A  T  S  O  A  K  I  L  T  M
```

voicesreading Grade 3

Name _____

Using an Apostrophe to Show Possession Proofread the paragraph. Circle the possessive words that are written incorrectly. Then, write the words correctly on the lines.

I had a great time visiting my aunts farm last weekend. Every morning, I helped her do chores. I made sure the three horses water was fresh and that all of the cows beds were clean. I collected the one chickens eggs, too. We woke up every morning to a birds song and fell asleep at night to the sound of many crickets tunes, too. I could see the stars much better in the country than in the city. As I rode home in my moms car, I smiled and thought about all of the fun I had on my Aunt Brendas farm.

1. _____   2. _____

3. _____   4. _____

5. _____   6. _____

7. _____   8. _____

Name _____

What Are the Characters' Plans? Think about the stories you have read. Choose one character from a story in the box, and complete the chart below.

> Secret Signs
> The Babe and I
> The Streets Are Free
>
> One Grain of Rice
> Candy Shop

Character: _____

Goal: _____

1. Values and skills the character needed: _____

_____

2. Person or people who helped the character: _____

_____

3. How the character reached his or her goal: _____

_____

_____

voicesreading Grade 3

Copyright © Zaner-Bloser, Inc.

Name _____

Long o Spelled oa, oe Circle the word that best completes each sentence.

I. I had a piece of _____ with butter and jam for breakfast.

toes   **toast**   **totes**   **tows**

2. We left our _____ in the garden because we were going to come back after lunch.

hoes   **house**   **how**   **hoarse**

3. We spent our summer along the _____ on the beach.

cows   **costs**   **coast**   **croak**

4. My grandma makes a pot _____ with potatoes and carrots.

roust   **roast**   **rows**   **roads**

5. Ouch! The horse stepped on my _____!

tow   **too**   **to**   **toe**

6. I was _____ after running home in the rain.

soaked   **sowed**   **socks**   **sold**

7. While I was hiking with my dad, I saw a _____ and her fawn.

do   **down**   **doe**   **does**

8. The _____ asked the players to work together as a team.

couch   **coat**   **close**   **coach**

Name _____

Spelling Words

coast	float	foam	hoe	moan	roast
soak	soap	throat	toad	toast	toe

Unscramble the letters in **dark print** to make a spelling word from the box. Write the words correctly on the lines.

l. noam _____

2. posa _____

3. eot _____

4. cosat _____

5. ohe _____

6. mofa _____

7. kosa _____

8. stroa _____

9. dota _____

10. stoat _____

ll. rhoatt _____

12. loaft _____

Now, write the spelling words from the box to answer each question.

13. Which words rhyme with **most**? _____

14. Which words can be verbs? _____

_____

15. Which words can be nouns? _____

_____

Name _____

Write the respelling from the box that matches each spelling word in **dark print**.

| /kōt/ | /flōt/ | /fōm/ | /hō/ | /mōn/ | /rōst/ |
| /sōk/ | /sōp/ | /tōd/ | /thrōt/ | /tōst/ | /tō/ |

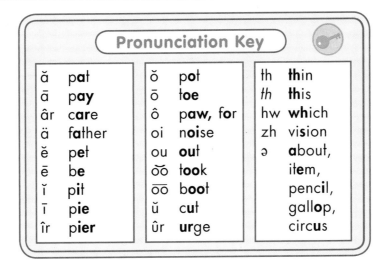

Pronunciation Key

ă	pat	ŏ	pot	th	thin
ā	pay	ō	toe	*th*	this
âr	care	ô	paw, for	hw	which
ä	father	oi	noise	zh	vision
ĕ	pet	ou	out	ə	about,
ē	be	ŏŏ	took		item,
ĭ	pit	ōō	boot		pencil,
ī	pie	ŭ	cut		gallop,
îr	pier	ûr	urge		circus

l. **coast** _____

2. **float** _____

3. **foam** _____

4. **hoe** _____

5. **moan** _____

6. **roast** _____

7. **soak** _____

8. **soap** _____

9. **throat** _____

10. **toad** _____

ll. **toast** _____

12. **toe** _____

Name _____

Replace the word or words in **dark print** with a vocabulary word from the box. Write the words on the lines.

hollow	navigate	smothered
ranchers	available	tips

1. I'll ask the doctor if he has any **useful information** on how to eat well.

   _____

2. Many **owners of large farms** are selling cattle this fall.

   _____

3. Julie likes her eggs **thickly covered** with cheese and gravy.

   _____

4. Is the car **able to be used** for our ski trip next weekend?

   _____

5. I am going to **carve out** the inside of this pumpkin so I can make a pie.

   _____

6. Pioneers had to **find the way** through the wilderness when they traveled on the Oregon Trail.

   _____

voicesreading Grade 3

Name _____

Compare and Contrast Think about the story **A Bus of Our Own**. How are the students alike? How are they different? Compare and contrast the differences between the students in the diagram below.

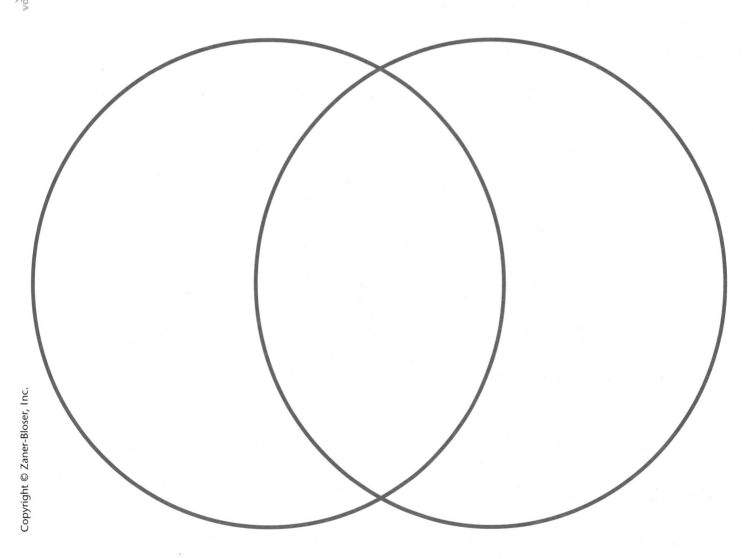

Name _____

Long i Spelled i, ie Circle the word in each sentence that has the **long i** sound spelled **i** or **ie**.

1.  Her sister could not find her favorite teddy bear.

2.  The pilot asked everyone to wear their safety belts for the trip.

3.  Mom baked an apple pie.

4.  The rind of the orange smells so good!

5. The tiger paced back and forth in the cage.

6.  Dad always wears a tie to work.

7.  We visit the island in the summer.

8.  Nick plays the violin in the school orchestra.

Name _____

Write the vocabulary word from the box that replaces the words in **dark print**.

eligible	objections	ridicule
maintain	agents	delay

1. I **keep the same** good grades at school because I work hard. _____

2. We have to have good grades to be **able** to play on the team. _____

3. I want to play basketball in spite of my friends' **expressions of disagreement**. _____

4. Their **words to insult** makes me upset sometimes. _____

5. We tried to start the game but there was a **condition of being put off**. _____

6. The **people who work for the government** want to watch the game, too. _____

Name _____

Topic Sentence and Supporting Details Read the paragraph. Circle the topic sentence. Underline the supporting details.

Every person has basic rights that should be protected. All people should have food and shelter. Everyone should be treated with dignity and respect. No one should have to live in fear or danger. We should all work together to be sure these basic rights are given to all people.

Now, write a topic sentence about the environment. Support the topic sentence with 3 or 4 supporting details.

_____

_____

_____

_____

_____

_____

_____

_____

Name _____

Long o Spelled oa, oe Complete the paragraph using the words from the box. Write the words on the lines. You will have to capitalize one word.

soaked	sailboats	coast	roasted	goats
road	toasty	floating	foamy	toes

As we drove along the _____, waves crashed

against the beach. The _____ twisted and turned as

we climbed higher and higher. Several _____

wandered across the road. _____ glided across the

ocean in the distance. We could see whales _____

in the warm water. I couldn't wait to bury my _____

in the hot sand. When we got to the beach, I jumped in the

_____ waves. When I was _____,

I rested in the sand until I was warm and _____.

That night, we made a fire and

_____ marshmallows.

It was a perfect summer day!

Name _____

Spelling Words

cider	lies	kind	mind	minus	pilot
pint	pioneer	science	silo	wild	wind

Circle the hidden spelling words.

```
K   I   N   K   I   N   D   M   I   N

O   M   L   I   E   S   L   P   E   S

M   I   N   D   P   I   L   I   E   I

I   N   D   W   E   L   D   O   Y   L

S   U   I   O   T   E   N   N   E   O

I   S   C   I   E   N   C   E   S   W

T   S   I   L   O   T   E   E   S   W

N   X   T   C   I   D   E   R   H   I

I   N   D   U   S   T   R   A   L   L

P   I   L   O   T   U   W   I   N   D
```

Name _____

Time Management Manage your time by following these tips:

- Make a list of activities in order of importance.
- Use your time wisely.
- Don't try to do too much.
- Know that there might be surprises.

Look at the list of things Susan needs to do this week. Write the activities on the calendar to make sure she has time for everything.

1. Piano lessons on Monday

2. Soccer practice on Tuesday

3. Free night

4. Social Studies test on Thursday

5. Spelling test on Friday

6. Soccer game on Saturday morning

7. Volunteer at an animal shelter.

8. Read three nights.

Sunday	Monday	Tuesday	Wednesday	Thursday	Friday	Saturday
5	6	7	8	9	10	11

Name _____

Expository   Read this example of an essay explaining a personal goal.

    My goal is to fly a jumbo jet. I know it is very difficult to become a jet pilot, but I can do it if I work hard. My first step will be to graduate from college. Next, I will learn how to fly a small airplane. When I have enough experience on small airplanes, I will teach others how to fly to get more experience. Finally, I will be ready to fly a jumbo jet. It takes many years and a lot of hard work to be a jet pilot, but I'm going to do it!

voicesreading Grade 3

Name _____

Prefixes pre- and mis- The prefix **pre-** means "before."
The prefix **mis-** means "wrongly" or "badly."

Examples: **prejudge** means "to judge before"
misspell means "to spell wrongly"

Add the prefix **pre-** or **mis-** to each word in **dark print** to make a word that matches each clue. Write the new word on the line.

I. to pay **before** _____

2. to **understand** wrongly _____

3. to **use** wrongly _____

4. to **cook** before _____

5. to **place** wrongly _____

6. to **treat** badly _____

7. to **test** before _____

8. to **write** before _____

9. to **lead** wrongly _____

10. to **judge** wrongly _____

II. to **heat** before _____

12. to **slice** before _____

Name _____

Draw a line from each vocabulary word in **dark print** to the definition it matches.

I. **remarkable**   brave and heroic

2. **outnumbered**   honored the memory of

3. **commended**   future outcomes

4. **gallant**   praised

5. **commemorated**   outmatched in number

6. **fortunes**   worth noticing or talking about

voicesreading Grade 3

Copyright © Zaner-Bloser, Inc.

Name _____

Compare and Contrast Think about the story **A Bus of Our Own**. In the story, some of the characters had to walk several miles to school. Compare and contrast your school day with the characters' school day.

My School Day	Mable Jean and Jeff's School Day

Name _____

Commas in a Series Read the sentences. Insert commas where they belong.

1. John Ben and Isaac are on the same team this year.

2. We saw monkeys tigers and giraffes at the zoo.

3. I will eat breakfast make my bed and do my chores today.

4. We went to a piano recital a soccer game and a birthday party last weekend.

5. I live in an apartment with my mother my grandma and my two cats.

6. Mom loves the colorful leaves in the fall fluffy snow in the winter and pretty flowers in the spring.

7. Dad asked me to vacuum dust and do the dishes after school.

8. Sheila has horses chickens and three baby sheep.

9. Tina likes to color with markers pencils and paints.

10. This weekend we are going to hike in the woods camp in the park and fish in the pond.

voicesreading Grade 3

Name _____

Spider Map You can use a Spider Map to organize your ideas for your essay.

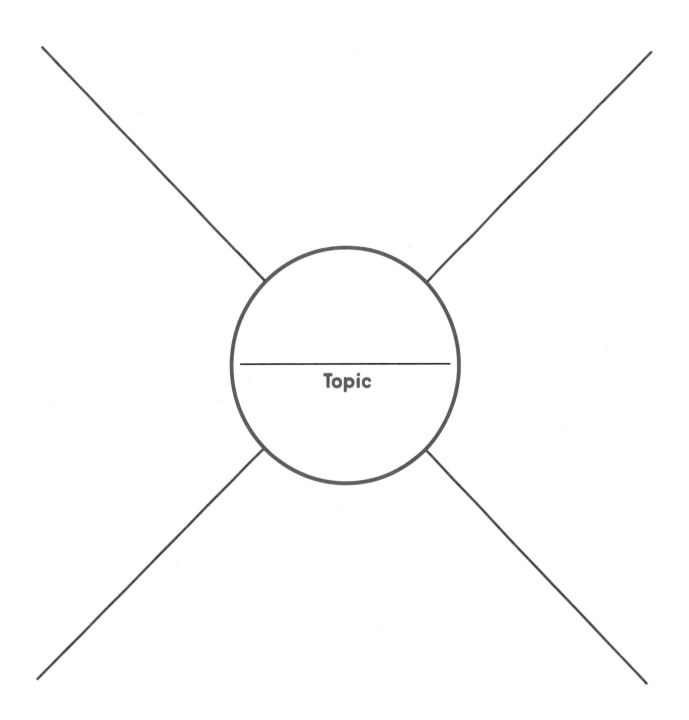

Topic

Name _____

Problems in My Community What is a problem you really care about? Think about the social problems you have read about and discussed this year. Choose one problem and complete the sentences below. Then interview your partner about the problem he or she chose.

I. Some social problems in my community are _____

_____

_____ .

2. One social problem I care about is _____

_____ .

3. I care about this problem because _____

_____

_____ .

4. I think the causes of this problem are _____

_____

_____

_____ .

voicesreading Grade 3

Copyright © Zaner-Bloser, Inc.

Name _____

Long i Spelled i, ie Read the words in each tic-tac-toe board. Draw a line through the three words in each board that have the **long i** sound spelled **i** or **ie**.

1.

film	mint	tiger
winter	giant	shine
kind	list	chin

2.

glitter	pie	five
find	pilot	visit
this	fiber	cider

3.

lie	bring	twist
pink	silo	sing
thing	misty	mind

4.

kindly	limp	children
child	finish	final
tie	pine	tinker

Name _____

Circle the misspelled words in each sentence and write them correctly on the lines.

I. I apologize for the lyes I told about you. _____

2. Grandma made hot apple sider for us. _____

3. Do you mynd if I take this seat next to you? _____

4. My brother is always kend to animals. _____

5. Our pillot landed the airplane on time. _____

6. The teacher said, "Twenty myness ten is ten." _____

7. Your great-grandfather was a pieonear who settled out West. _____

8. "Could I please have another pient of milk?" asked Oliver. _____

9. He turned the former cylo into a place to keep hay. _____

10. I really enjoy ciance, especially astronomy. _____

11. The wynd blowing from the cold North Sea chills my bones. _____

12. It is always best to leave wyald animals in their natural homes. _____

Name _____

Suffixes -ly and -ful Add **-ly** or **-ful** to a word from the box to make a word that completes each sentence. Write the new word on the line.

quick	care	truth	foolish
cheer	help	wonder	thank

I. Grandma asked me to be very _____ with her teacups.

2. The friendly dog always has a _____ twinkle in his eyes.

3. She _____ finished her breakfast and rushed outside.

4. I was _____ when my best friend helped me study for the test.

5. It's best to be _____ and say you're sorry when you do something wrong.

6. We had a _____ day baking cookies with Aunt Andie.

7. I _____ left my homework in my locker.

8. "Thank you for being so _____!" Mrs. Ati said after I shoveled the snow in her driveway.

Name _____

Use this checklist when you revise your writing.

Revising Checklist: Expository

yes	no	Does the introduction make the readers want to read more?
yes	no	Does each paragraph have important information?
yes	no	Does my essay describe the goal and list how I will reach it?
yes	no	Does my essay have a clear introduction, body, and conclusion?
yes	no	Do time-order words show the steps to reaching the goal?
yes	no	Does every sentence begin with a capital letter and end with the correct punctuation?
yes	no	Are commas used in a series correctly?

voicesreading Grade 3

Copyright © Zaner-Bloser, Inc.

Name _____

Circle the vocabulary word that best completes each sentence.

I. We had _____ to Mrs. Wong's plan to give us a test on Friday.

agents   **objections**   **phrases**   **vibrations**

2. I must _____ good grades if I want to go on the ski trip.

maintain   **delay**   **signal**   **reserve**

3. I could feel the _____ of my sister because I still suck my thumb.

ridicule   **refuge**   **fortunate**   **cowards**

4. The passengers endured a long _____, but they were patient.

refuge   **awakening**   **trial**   **delay**

5. You must play an instrument to be _____ for the band.

fortunate   **flawless**   **eligible**   **smart**

6. The government will send _____ to investigate the crime.

ranchers   **milestones**   **agents**   **tips**

Name _____

Write the vocabulary word to replace the words in **dark print**.

gallant	**commended**	**commemorated**
outnumbered	**fortunes**	**remarkable**

1. The woman made a **brave** effort to save the plate of spaghetti from falling on the floor. _____

2. The Grand Canyon is a place that is truly **worth noticing**. _____

3. We **honored the memory of** Charles Lindbergh in a ceremony by the sea. _____

4. The boys **outmatched in number** the girls in the class. _____

5. The general **praised** the soldier for his bravery in battle. _____

6. When we finished school, I wondered what our **future outcomes** would be. _____

Name _____

Problem and Solution Think about the story **A Bus of Our Own**. Answer the questions.

I. What is the problem in the story?

_____

_____

2. Why is this a problem?

_____

_____

3. How is the problem solved?

_____

_____

4. How is the solution unfair?

_____

_____

5. How do you think the problem could have been solved?

_____

_____

Name _____

Points of View Think about the story **Teammates**. Complete the web using information from the story. Tell about the characters' points of view about the topic.

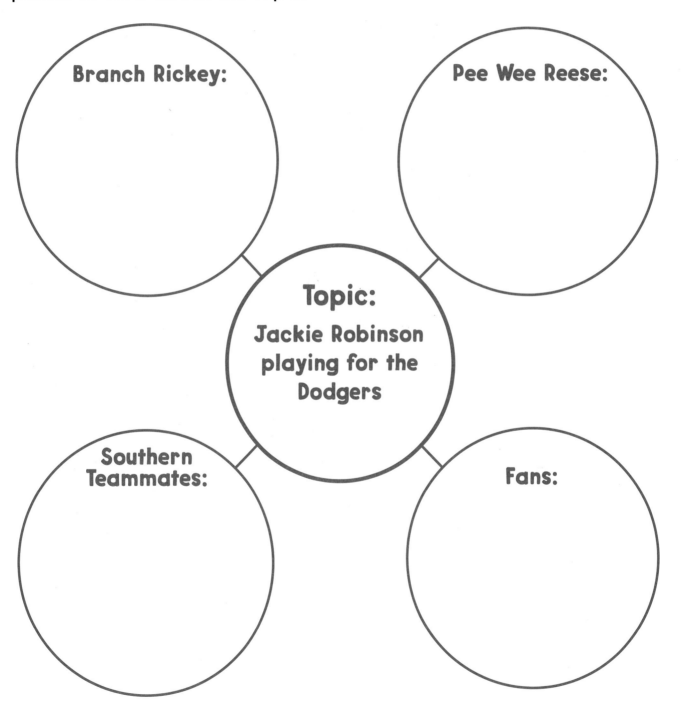

voicesreading Grade 3

Name _____

Words With qu Write a word from the box to complete each group.

quit	quiz	quart	question	quick
quarter	quake	quarrel	quack	queen

1. fast, speedy, _____

2. test, question, _____

3. nickel, dime, _____

4. pint, gallon, _____

5. moo, oink, _____

6. princess, dutchess, _____

7. fight, argue, _____

8. stop, drop out, _____

9. shake, tremble, _____

10. ask, query, _____

Name _____

Write the vocabulary word from the box that matches each definition.

brightened	decades	excelled
reliable	oppose	refuge

1. periods of ten years   _____

2. became very good at   _____

3. protection   _____

4. to disagree with   _____

5. became better   _____

6. steady or consistent   _____

Now, write a poem using as many vocabulary words as you can.

_____

_____

_____

_____

voicesreading Grade 3

Name _____

Explanatory Paragraph An **explanatory paragraph** tells how to do something. A clear explanatory paragraph includes a topic sentence that tells what the paragraph is about. The next sentence should list materials or ingredients, if needed. Detail sentences give step-by-step instructions. Time-order words provide clarity.

Choose a topic from the box. Write a topic sentence and then write an explanatory paragraph about the topic.

> **How to Plan a Birthday Party**
> **How to Organize a School Project**
> **How to Sell Lemonade**
> **How to Make Pizza**

_____

_____

_____

_____

_____

_____

Name _____

Long i Spelled i, ie Circle the word that names each picture.

 I.
tip
tie
time
try

2.
tiger
trigger
thief
timber

 3.
pill
pry
pie
ply

4.
pillow
piles
pilot
please

 5.
tilt
title
tickle
tidal

6.
line
link
lint
lion

 7.
siren
circle
syrup
cereal

8.
violet
village
violin
violet

 9.
higher
hiker
helper
hitter

10.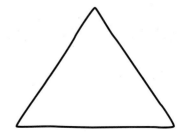
triangle
trick
twice
twinkle

Name _____

Spelling Words

quack quart quarter quarterback queen question
quick quiet quill quit quite quiz

Unscramble the letters in **dark print** to make spelling words from the box. Write the words correctly on the lines.

1. terquarback _____
2. ionquest _____
3. illqu _____
4. teuiq _____
5. kuacq _____
6. quzi _____
7. tarqu _____
8. aqurter _____
9. enque _____
10. tequi _____
11. uqti _____
12. iquck _____

voicesreading Grade 3

Name _____

Reading a Key Look at the map. Use the key to answer the questions.

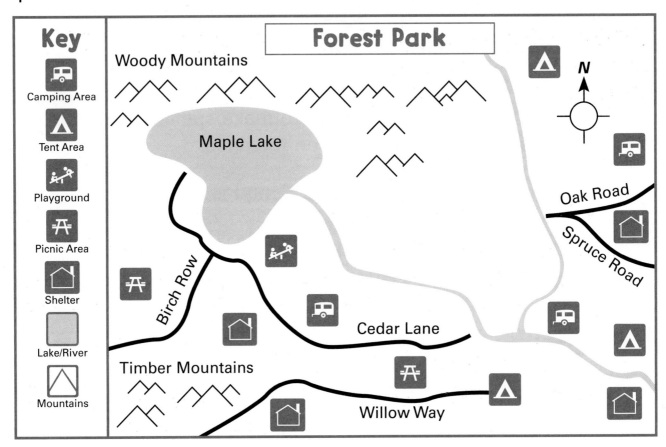

1. Does this park have canoeing areas? _____

2. Which mountain range is near Willow Way? _____

3. What does 🚐 mean? _____

4. Is there a picnic area north of Oak Road? _____

5. Which road leads to the playground? _____

6. How many shelters are at Forest Park? _____

Name _____

Suffixes -less and -ness   The suffix **-less** means "without" or "lacking." The suffix **-ness** means "state," "quality," or "condition."

Examples: **priceless** means "without price"

happiness means "the state of being happy"

Add the suffix **-less** or **-ness** to each word from the box to complete each sentence. Write the new word on the line.

help	red	harm
cloud	sad	rest

1. I felt _____ as the glass slipped and crashed to the floor.

2. The _____ sky and warm sunshine made it a perfect day.

3. I could see my brother's _____ when his best friend moved away.

4. My dog has a loud bark, but she's really _____.

5. The _____ in her cheeks was caused by embarrassment.

6. My sister gets _____ when she has to sit still.

Name _____

Complete the crossword puzzle with the vocabulary words from the box.

| permanent | uncertain | spiked |
| register | requires | improvements |

Across
1. changes for the better
4. to sign up for
6. not sure

Down
2. meant to last
3. hit at a steep angle
5. demands; calls for

voicesreading Grade 3

Name _____

Points of View Think about the story **Teammates**. Tell what you think each character was thinking when Jackie Robinson stepped onto the baseball field for the first time.

1. Jackie Robinson: _____

_____

2. Branch Rickey: _____

_____

3. Pee Wee Reese: _____

_____

4. Fans: _____

_____

5. Teammates: _____

_____

Name _____

Comparing With Adjectives Circle the word that best completes each sentence.

I. I am the (**younger, youngest**) person in my family.

2. Our dog is (**younger, youngest**) than our cat.

3. We live in the (**older, oldest**) house in our neighborhood.

4. The school building is (**older, oldest**) than our house is.

5. My grandparents have the (**prettier, prettiest**) rose bushes I have ever seen.

6. Their roses are even (**prettier, prettiest**) than the roses at the park.

7. Amy is the (**nicer, nicest**) person I know.

8. I ran the (**faster, fastest**) in the race last weekend.

9. I hope to run (**faster, fastest**) each time I race.

10. The windows are (**dirtier, dirtiest**) than I've ever seen them.

Name _____

Community Responsibility What is one solution to a social problem you care about? What can people do together to support this solution? Complete the sentences below.

I. The social problem I care about is _____

_____

_____ .

2. The causes of this problem are _____

_____

_____ .

3. One solution to this problem is _____

_____

_____ .

4. The community can help solve this problem by _____

_____

_____

_____ .

Name _____

Words With qu Write the word from the box that matches each clue.

voicesreading Grade 3

quick	quarter	quit	question	queen
quiz	quack	quarterback	quilt	quiet

I. twenty-five cents _____

2. a king's wife _____

3. duck talk _____

4. fast _____

5. a type of blanket _____

6. the opposite of **loud** _____

7. a football player _____

8. to stop _____

9. to test _____

10. the opposite of **answer** _____

Name _____

Spelling Words

quack	quart	quarter	quarterback
queen	question	quick	quiet
quill	quit	quite	quiz

Write the spelling word from the box that matches each respelling. Use the pronunciation key to help you.

1. /**kwôr´** tər/ _____

2. /kwôrt/ _____

3. /**kwĕs´** chən/ _____

4. /kwăk/ _____

5. /**kwī´** ĭt/ _____

6. /**kwôr´** tər băk/ _____

7. /kwēn/ _____

8. /kwīt/ _____

9. /kwĭz/ _____

10. /kwĭl/ _____

11. /kwĭt/ _____

12. /kwĭk/ _____

Pronunciation Key

ă	pat	ŏ	pot	th	thin
ā	pay	ō	toe	*th*	this
âr	care	ô	paw, for	hw	which
ä	father	oi	noise	zh	vision
ĕ	pet	ou	out	ə	about,
ē	be	o͝o	took		item,
ĭ	pit	o͞o	boot		pencil,
ī	pie	ŭ	cut		gallop,
îr	pier	ûr	urge		circus

Quack !

Name _____

Prefixes pre- and mis- Add **pre-** or **mis-** to a word from the box to complete each sentence. Write the new word on the line. You will have to capitalize one word.

write	heat	mixed	behaves
pay	judge	places	understood

I. _____ the oven before you bake the potatoes.

2. I had to _____ before I pumped the gas.

3. My father often _____ his wallet and car keys.

4. I _____ the directions and couldn't find my way to the store.

5. My stories are usually better if I _____ them before I write the final drafts.

6. It's not a good idea to _____ others before getting to know them.

7. My dog often _____ if we leave her alone for too long.

8. I _____ the ingredients so I could bake them later.

Name _____

Write the vocabulary words from the box to complete the paragraph.

brightened	decades	excelled
reliable	oppose	refuge

I could tell my grandfather was happy to see me because his

face _____ when I walked into his hospital room.

He knew how much I loved and looked up to him. As a younger

man, he _____ in school. After becoming a

lawyer, he worked with the civil rights movement for three

_____. He was always _____.

People knew that he would always try his best and never give up.

He gave _____ to those who needed safety. He

helped _____ racism

and hatred. He will always be

my hero. I hope he gets

well soon!

voicesreading Grade 3

Name _____

Write the vocabulary word from the box that best completes each sentence.

improvements	spiked	uncertain
permanent	register	requires

1. The player _____ the volleyball over the net.

2. I am _____ about what to wear to the party.

3. Be sure to _____ to vote when you turn eighteen years old.

4. Many nations worked together to build a _____ base on the South Pole.

5. Mrs. Sidbeck _____ her students to read for at least an hour every night.

6. The school felt warmer after they made _____ to the building.

Copyright © Zaner-Bloser, Inc.

Name _____

Compare and Contrast Compare the way the teammates treated Jackie with the way that Pee Wee treated Jackie.

Pee Wee	Teammates
1.	
2.	
3.	

Name _____

Evaluate Think about the story **Passage to Freedom**. Complete the chart with information from the story.

Action	Why the Action Happened
1.	
2.	
3.	
4.	

Name _____

Words With igh Write the word from the box that best completes each sentence.

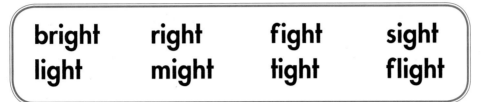

bright	right	fight	sight
light	might	tight	flight

1. The cats often _____ over their toys.

2. My sister does not leave my mother's _____ when we are at the store.

3. My shoes are getting _____. I think I need a new pair.

4. I _____ be allowed to come over this weekend after I finish my chores.

5. I write with my left hand, but my dad writes with his _____ hand.

6. The airplane rushed down the runway and smoothly took _____.

7. The sunshine was so _____, I had to cover my eyes.

8. I turned on the _____ so that I could find my book.

Name _____

Write the vocabulary word from the box that matches each definition.

threats	fugitive	evidence
devoted	mercy	engage

1. promises of harm or punishment   _____

2. kindness   _____

3. to participate in; to become involved   _____

4. a group of facts; proof   _____

5. about a person who is running away   _____

6. gave; dedicated   _____

Now, use the vocabulary words in complete sentences.

7. _____

8. _____

9. _____

10. _____

11. _____

12. _____

voicesreading Grade 3

Copyright © Zaner-Bloser, Inc.

Name _____

Avoiding Sentence Fragments Read each group of words. Write **C** if the words make a **complete sentence.** If the words make a **fragment,** write words to make a complete sentence on the line.

1. Needed jelly, peanut butter, and a few other things.

_____

2. Mixed the ingredients together in a jar.

_____

3. The bubbly mixture.

_____

4. Then they went out for dinner.

_____

5. They had pizza and ice cream, and then they went home.

_____

6. When they returned to their school.

_____

7. The science experiment.

_____

8. All over the counter and the floor.

_____

Name _____

Words With qu Circle the word that best completes each sentence.

1. The teacher asked us to be _____ while we took the test.

   quite   **quit**   **quiet**   **quiz**

2. I had a _____ about when the homework was due.

   quest   **question**   **quit**   **queasy**

3. I told my little brother I would pay him a _____ if he helped me clean my room.

   quarter   **quart**   **quality**   **quack**

4. The _____ arrived at the party in a limo.

   quest   **quit**   **queen**   **quiz**

5. I studied for the _____ and got all but one answer correct.

   quill   **quiz**   **quit**   **quiet**

6. The duck grabbed the bits of bread and made a loud _____.

   quote   **quart**   **quiet**   **quack**

7. I included a _____ from Martin Luther King Jr. in my paper.

   quote   **quart**   **quarter**   **quill**

8. Tara said I should _____ biting my nails.

   quit   **quest**   **queen**   **quill**

voicesreading Grade 3

Name _____

Spelling Words

delight	might	sight	fight	right	bright
high	sigh	sight brightly	flight	night	light

Write the list of spelling words in **ABC order**.

1. _____   2. _____

3. _____   4. _____

5. _____   6. _____

7. _____   8. _____

9. _____   10. _____

11. _____   12. _____

voicesreading Grade 3

Copyright © Zaner-Bloser, Inc.

Name _____

Reading a Map Answer the questions about the map.

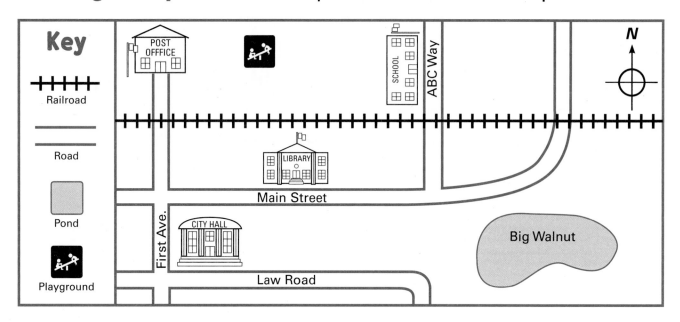

voicesreading Grade 3

I. On which street is the post office located? _____

2. What is the name of the pond? _____

3. In which direction would you travel
   to get from city hall to the library? _____

4. What is located on ABC Way? _____

5. How many streets does the railroad cross? _____

6. Is there a park near the pond? _____

7. Where is the playground located? _____

   _____

8. On which street is city hall located? _____

Name _____

Dividing Words With Prefixes and Suffixes Divide words into syllables between the prefixes or suffixes and the base words.

Examples: re/read/ing
un/earth/ly

Write the words from the box in **ABC order**. Draw a line between the syllables in each word.

careless	harmful	misspelling	prejudge
unpacking	reuse	retelling	lovely
priceless	mistake	joyful	preheat

I. _____   2. _____

3. _____   4. _____

5. _____   6. _____

7. _____   8. _____

9. _____   10. _____

II. _____   12. _____

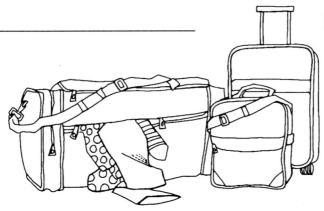

Name _____

Draw a line to match each vocabulary word in **dark print** to its definition.

1. **revere**

2. **uprooted**

3. **miraculous**

4. **awakening**

5. **sling**

6. **lame**

pulled or removed a plant or tree from the soil

to think of someone with deep admiration or respect

a sudden realization

caused by a supernatural event

unable to walk well

a piece of cloth tied around the neck, used to support an injured arm

Name _____

Evaluate Think about the story **Passage to Freedom**. Answer the questions.

I. What will happen to the people waiting outside the fence if Sugihara does not help them?

_____

2. Why is the decision to help the people difficult for Sugihara to make?

_____

_____

3. Why did Sugihara want to write all of the visas himself?

_____

_____

4. Why did Sugihara continue handing out visas even from the train window?

_____

_____

5. What would you do if you were Sugihara?

_____

_____

Name _____

Using I or Me Write the words from the box to complete the sentences.

> **I**   **me**   **Alecia**

I. _____ and _____ have known each other forever.

2. My parents gave _____ and _____ matching necklaces.

3. Mom told _____ and _____ that a good friend is a treasure.

4. _____ and _____ tell each other secrets.

5. _____ and _____ like the same books.

6. _____ and _____ have agreed that we will always tell each other the truth.

7. Dad reads to _____ and _____ when we have sleepovers.

8. _____ and _____ are the best friends ever.

Character Development Practice

Name ____

My Helping Plan Think about how you can help solve the social problem you care about. Complete the chart below and share your answers with your partner.

Social Problem: ______________________________

Three Things I Can Do to Help Solve the Problem:

Action 1: ______________________________

____

____

____

Action 2: ______________________________

____

____

____

Action 3: ______________________________

____

____

____

Name _____

Words With igh Proofread the sentences. Circle the misspelled word. Rewrite the word correctly on the line.

1. The kite flew so high that it was no longer in site.   _____

2. The lite blinked on and off to warn boats that a storm was coming.   _____

3. It is better to end a fite with words than with fists.   _____

4. I don't like it when my shoes are too tite.   _____

5. I pushed with all of my mite, but the rock would not budge.   _____

6. The bats took flite as soon as the sky was dark.   _____

7. I stayed up too late last nite to watch a movie.   _____

8. Sometimes it can be hard to do the rite thing.   _____

9. If you turn slitely to the right, you'll see the statue.   _____

10. The brite lights made me squint.   _____

voicesreading Grade 3

Copyright © Zaner-Bloser, Inc.

Name _____

Spelling Words

bright	brightly	delight	fight	flight	high
light	might	night	right	sigh	sight

Unscramble the letters in **dark print** to make spelling words from the box.

1. **gisht** _____

2. **rightbly** _____

3. **ghih** _____

4. **fgiht** _____

5. **tighn** _____

6. **griht** _____

7. **ightl** _____

8. **gish** _____

9. **fghilt** _____

10. **htmig** _____

11. **ribght** _____

12. **lightde** _____

voicesreading Grade 3

Name _____

Suffixes -less and -ness Add the suffix **-less** or **-ness** to each word in **dark print** to make a word that matches each clue. Write the new word on the line.

1. without **help** _____

2. the state of being **sloppy** _____

3. the state of being **sad** _____

4. without **care** _____

5. without **fear** _____

6. the state of being **happy** _____

7. the state of being **neat** _____

8. without **harm** _____

9. without **rest** _____

10. the state of being **soft** _____

11. without **pain** _____

12. the state of being **loud** _____

Name _____

Circle the vocabulary word that best completes each sentence.

1. _____ did not frighten Rosa Parks, so she stayed in her seat at the front of the bus.

   Decades   **Threats**   **Evidence**   **Mercies**

2. Our teacher said we should _____ ourselves in life with energy and joy.

   engage   **oppose**   **ridicule**   **target**

3. The _____ slave who ran away from her owner hid for several months.

   reliable   **eligible**   **outnumbered**   **fugitive**

4. You show _____ when you forgive someone who hurt your feelings.

   ceremony   **access**   **mercy**   **threat**

5. Scientists find _____ to explain how things work.

   vibrations   **objections**   **mercy**   **evidence**

6. I _____ a great deal of time to studying for the test.

   devoted   **commended**   **registered**   **spiked**

Name _____

Write the vocabulary word that best completes each sentence.

sling	lame	miraculous
uprooted	awakening	revere

1. The frog was _____ because its leg was caught in a trap.

2. It was _____ that the glasses in the box didn't break during the move.

3. Hoshi _____ the bush and replanted it closer to the house.

4. Reading books will lead to an _____ that can change your life.

5. The nurse put my arm in a cast and a _____ because I broke a bone.

6. I _____ Mrs. Reese because I think she is a good role model.

Name _____

Points of View Think about the story **Passage to Freedom**. Answer the questions.

I. Who tells the story?

_____

2. How did the son feel about what his father did for the people?

_____

_____

_____

3. How did the people outside the fence feel while they were waiting for Sugihara's decision?

_____

_____

_____

4. How did the son feel after he understood what had happened?

_____

_____

_____

Name _____

Noting Details Think about the story **A River Ran Wild**.
Complete the charts with details from the story.

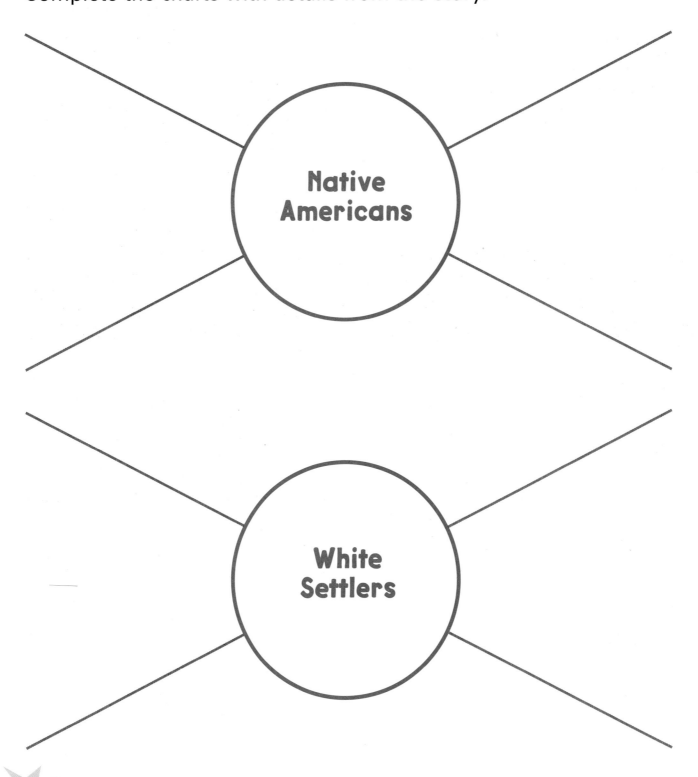

Name _____

VCCCV Words Write the word from the box that names each picture.

pumpkin	sandwich	pilgrim	mattress
pitcher	children	branch	lobster

1. _____

2. _____

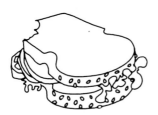

3. _____

4. _____

5. _____

6. _____

7. _____

8. _____

Name _____

Write the vocabulary word from the box that best completes each group of words.

accumulate	isolated	massive
critic	abundant	prospered

I. large, heavy, huge, __ __ __ __◯__ __

2. alone, away, lonely, ◯__ __ __ __ __ __ __

3. store, collect, gather, __◯◯__ __ __ __ __ __ __

4. much, full, ample, __ __ __ __ __ __ ◯__

5. grew, became rich, thrived, __◯__ __ __ __ __ __ __

Now, write the letters that are circled above. Unscramble the letters to write the vocabulary word that matches the definition below.

__ __ __ __ __ __

6. somebody who speaks out against something _____

voicesreading Grade 3

Name _____

Giving Examples and Reasons Read the topic sentence below.
Write 5 good examples or reasons that support the topic.

> **Topic:** **How can we work together as a community to stand up for our rights?**

_____

_____

_____

_____

_____

_____

_____

_____

Name _____

Words With igh   Circle the word that best completes each sentence.

1. I _____ with relief when I found my glasses.

   sight   **sighed**   **silent**   **straight**

2. I would be _____ if you could come to the movies with me.

   decided   **rightly**   **delighted**   **slightly**

3. Let's shake hands and make up instead of _____.

   fighting   **lighting**   **freight**   **frighten**

4. I go _____ home after school so Grandpa doesn't worry.

   sight   **sigh**   **right**   **slight**

5. This light is too _____!

   bright   **right**   **tight**   **light**

6. Mom _____ the candle on the table when we eat dinner.

   sights   **brights**   **lights**   **tights**

7. Chloe wore pink _____ for her ballet recital.

   tomatoes   **tides**   **straight**   **tights**

8. My sister said my messy room was a _____.

   fright   **fight**   **freight**   **fried**

voicesreading Grade 3

Name _____

Spelling Words

alphabet	angle	answer	burglar
butcher	children	exchange	explain
grandfather	hundred	lobster	pilgrim

Circle the hidden spelling words.

```
A  L  P  H  A  B  E  T  C  H  A  L
A  N  G  E  L  U  H  I  A  L  O  P
A  N  G  R  A  T  D  R  E  B  E  I
G  E  T  L  U  C  C  B  S  U  X  L
X  Y  Z  U  E  H  A  T  T  R  P  G
G  R  A  N  D  E  E  O  R  G  L  R
C  H  I  L  D  R  A  N  F  L  A  I
E  X  C  H  A  N  G  E  P  A  I  M
H  U  N  D  R  E  D  T  O  R  N  U
C  H  I  L  D  R  E  N  A  R  E  T
H  E  A  N  S  W  E  R  T  O  M  Y
G  R  A  N  D  F  A  T  H  E  R  I
```

Name _____

> **Using the Internet** The **Internet** is a useful tool for finding information. **Key words** help you find the information you need.
>
> **Example:** **Topic:** Helping Your Community
>
> **Key words:** community projects, community programs, helping the needy

Write the key words you might use to find information about each topic on the Internet.

I. Snails That Live in Utah _____

2. A Vacation Place _____

3. How to Care for an Iguana _____

4. Rome's History _____

5. The Different Dog Breeds _____

6. The Types of Trees in My Town _____

7. A Recipe With Chicken _____

8. Movie Times at the Theater _____

voicesreading Grade 3

Name _____

Expository   Read this example of a letter to the editor about a community's problem.

75 Granger Street
Oak Park, OH 43034
June 5, 2007

Dear Editor,

My name is Emerson, and I am in the third grade at Granger Elementary. Our city has a problem. Cars are driving too fast on Best Street. My friends and I cross the street a lot, and the drivers don't pay attention! Our street can be safe. If drivers followed the speed limit, we would feel safer about crossing the street.

The city can do three things to solve this problem. First, it can put speed bumps on the street. Then it should add more signs that show that children live and walk in the area. Finally, the police officers could spend more time in the area watching for people who drive too fast. We need to solve the problem before someone gets hurt.

Sincerely,
Emerson Sprout

Name _____

voicesreading Grade 3

Dividing VCCCV Words Divide VCCCV words with three-letter blends between the first and second consonant. If the word has a digraph, the digraph always stays together.

Examples: ham/ster (three-letter blend)
pick/le (digraph)

Rewrite each word in **dark print** and draw a line between the syllables.

1. **conflict** _____

2. **lobster** _____

3. **instead** _____

4. **trample** _____

5. **distrust** _____

6. **improve** _____

7. **athlete** _____

8. **subtract** _____

9. **complex** _____

10. **conflict** _____

11. **panther** _____

12. **pumpkin** _____

Name _____

Draw a line from each vocabulary word to the definition it matches.

I. **frequent**   a set of laws passed by the government

2. **domesticated**   relating to the protection of health

3. **contaminated**   encouraged

4. **motivated**   unclean

5. **sanitary**   trained to live near people

6. **legislation**   occurring often

Now, use each vocabulary word in a complete sentence.

7. _____

8. _____

9. _____

10. _____

II. _____

12. _____

Name _____

Noting Details Think about the story **A River Ran Wild**. In the story, Oweana has a very vivid dream that causes him to take action and save the river. Write a paragraph about a dream you've had. Include vivid details from the dream.

_____

_____

_____

_____

_____

_____

_____

Now, draw a picture of your dream.

voicesreading Grade 3

Name _____

Commas After Introductory Words Read the sentences. Add commas where they belong.

1. No I am not going to the party tomorrow.

2. Well she did say I could borrow her computer.

3. Henry please turn the light off when you leave the room.

4. Yes I am very happy my grandma is visiting!

5. Well at least it will rain for only one day.

6. Riley would you mind taking a message to the office?

7. Yes I would be happy to help you with your homework.

8. No I didn't know that geckos have sticky feet.

9. James I'm glad to see you're feeling better today.

10. Well the test wasn't as hard as I thought it was!

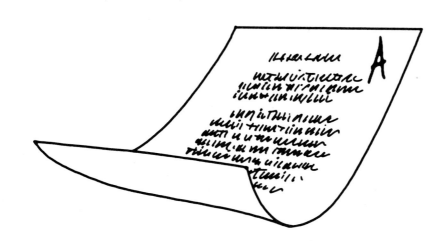

Name _____

Main Idea Table You can use a Main Idea Table to organize your ideas for your letter to the editor.

voicesreading Grade 3

Main Idea:

Supporting Detail:

Supporting Detail:

Supporting Detail:

Supporting Detail:

Name _____

My Speech Think about a social problem you want to solve. Complete the sentences below and use the answers to write your speech.

Opening

1. I will introduce the problem by _____.

Social Problem

2. The social problem I care about is _____

_____.

3. I want to solve this problem because _____

_____.

Causes

4. The causes of this problem are _____.

Solution

5. The best solution is _____.

Appeal to the Audience

6. One way the audience can help is _____.

Conclusion

7. I will conclude my speech about the social problem by

_____.

Name _____

VCCCV Words Choose the word from the box that best completes each sentence.

pitcher	athlete	improve
subtract	instead	conflict

1. Mr. Hawkins is a good _____ because he gets plenty of exercise.

2. I had to _____ money from my allowance to buy my sister a present.

3. May I have a banana _____ of an orange?

4. My grades will _____ if I spend more time studying.

5. The best way to solve a _____ is to talk about it.

6. Aunt Mary keeps the _____ of lemonade in the refrigerator.

voices**reading** Grade 3

Name _____

Proofread the sentences. Circle the misspelled word in each sentence and write it correctly on the line.

1. My granfather gave me good advice about how to be kind. _____

2. The bucher is a friendly man who likes to sing. _____

3. My friend has a pet laubster named Caleb. _____

4. I learned the alfabet by singing the ABC song. _____

5. All of the childran danced around the room. _____

6. The pillgram made a brave decision to start a new life. _____

7. My great-grandma is almost one hundread years old. _____

8. Lucy, could you please explane this math problem to me? _____

9. Please awnser the phone with a friendly voice. _____

10. The bergaler dressed like Santa Claus and tried to go down the chimney. _____

11. The bridge formed a sharp angel over the bay. _____

12. Would you like to exchanj your sandwich for my bagel? _____

Name _____

Dividing Words With Prefixes and Suffixes Add a prefix and/or suffix from the box to each word in **dark print**. Write the new words on the line. Then, draw a line between the base words and suffixes or prefixes. (**Hint:** All prefixes and suffixes will be used more than once.)

voicesreading Grade 3

> Suffixes: -ful   -less   -y   -ly   -able   -ish
>
> Prefixes: -mis   -un   -pre   -dis   -re

1. gentle _____

2. color _____

3. happy _____

4. agree _____

5. cloud _____

6. friend _____

7. green _____

8. trust _____

9. place _____

10. believe _____

Name _____

Use this checklist when you revise your writing.

Revising Checklist: Persuasive

| yes | no | Does the letter have a **heading, inside address, greeting, body, closing,** and **signature**? |

| yes | no | Is the opinion stated in the first and last paragraphs? |

| yes | no | Is a summary of reasons for the opinion in the first paragraph? |

| yes | no | Is each reason listed in the order of importance? |

| yes | no | Does the letter have many details, facts, and examples to give a strong argument? |

| yes | no | Does every sentence begin with a capital letter and end with the correct punctuation? |

| yes | no | Are commas after introductory words used correctly? |

Name _____

Write the vocabulary word from the box that replaces the words in **dark print**.

accumulate	isolated	massive
critic	abundant	prospered

I. If you save your money, it may **pile up** and become a small fortune.

_____

2. The **large and heavy** jumbo jet slowly flew off the runway.

_____

3. Fresh apples were **present in large quantities** this fall at the orchard.

_____

4. The business owner knew he had **become wealthy** because his name was in the paper.

_____

5. They called me a **person who speaks out against something** because I did not like the movie.

_____

6. Julia likes to spend time **far away from others** in a cabin.

_____

voicesreading Grade 3

Copyright © Zaner-Bloser, Inc.

Name _____

Write the vocabulary word from the box that best completes each sentence in the paragraph.

frequent	legislation	domesticated
sanitary	contaminated	motivated

We need to take care of our lakes and rivers. We should be

_____ to keep them clean and healthy. One way

we can help is to follow the rules or _____

about throwing things away. Sometimes, our waterways are

_____ because people break the rules and throw

garbage into the water. We need to help make the water more

_____ for the animals that live in the wild.

Not all animals are _____, so they rely on the

environment for their food and shelter. We need to make sure

throwing garbage where it doesn't belong doesn't become a

_____ event.

Name _____

Evaluate Read the questions about the story **A River Ran Wild**. Write the answers on the lines.

l. How did the Native Americans treat the river and the land

around it? _____

_____

2. How did the white settlers treat the land? _____

_____

3. Why did the Native Americans call the river "River with the

Pebbled Bottom"? _____

_____

4. Why did the Native Americans and white settlers fight for one

hundred years?_____

_____

_____

5. How does the author feel about the way the people treated

the river?_____

6. How would the river look if Oweana had not had a goal to help

the river?_____

_____

Name _____

Cause and Effect Think about the story ¡Si, Se Puede! Yes, We Can! Complete the chart with information from the story.

Cause	Effect
I.	
2.	
3.	
4.	
5.	

Name _____

Words With ough Write the words from the box in the correct column.

bought	cough	though	sought	rough	fought
enough	thorough	tough	dough	although	thought

Short o Spelled ough	Long o Spelled ough	Short u Spelled ough
_____	_____	_____
_____	_____	_____
_____	_____	_____
_____	_____	_____
_____	_____	_____

Now, use one word from each column in a complete sentence.

1. _____

2. _____

3. _____

voicesreading Grade 3

Copyright © Zaner-Bloser, Inc.

Name _____

Write the vocabulary word from the box that best completes each group of words.

outgoing	ironic	zeal
united	ethnic	outspoken

1. friendly, sociable, likeable, _____

2. confident, bold, brave, _____

3. joined, mixed, together, _____

4. racial, religious, national, _____

5. devotion, enthusiasm, eagerness, _____

6. opposite, surprising, unexpected, _____

Now, use each vocabulary word in a complete sentence.

7. _____

8. _____

9. _____

10. _____

11. _____

12. _____

Name _____

Compare and Contrast Paragraph When you write a compare and contrast paragraph, you are explaining how two things are alike or different. Follow the steps below to write a compare and contrast paragraph.

I. Choose two things to compare. _____

_____

_____

2. Write a topic sentence that tells what you are comparing and how the two things are alike or different. _____

_____

_____

3. Write three or four detail sentences that support the topic sentence. _____

_____

_____

_____

_____

voicesreading Grade 3

Name _____

VCCCV Words Circle the word that best completes each sentence.

I. I like packing my lunch _____ of buying it at school.

    instant   **insist**   **instead**   **intend**

2. We saw a tank full of _____ at the aquarium.

    lodges   **lobsters**   **locals**   **lockets**

3. I am working hard at swim practice so I can _____.

    important   **imitate**   **imagine**   **improve**

4. I made my sister a peanut butter and jelly _____ for lunch.

    sandwich   **saddle**   **sample**   **sandbox**

5. I drew a silly face on my _____.

    puddle   **punch**   **pumpkin**   **punish**

6. The _____ threw three strikes in a row, and the crowd cheered.

    picture   **pitch**   **pincher**   **pitcher**

7. The _____ were very brave to make such a dangerous voyage.

    pilgrims   **pillars**   **pillows**   **pickles**

8. My dog and cat seem to have a _____ almost every day.

    constant   **conflict**   **corner**   **confuse**

Name _____

Spelling Words

bought	brought	dough	fought
ought	though	thought	

Follow the directions to complete each word with the letters **ough**. Use the spelling words from the box.

1. + d   ___ ough

2. + t   ough ___

3. + th + t   ___ ___ ough ___

4. + th   ___ ___ ough

5. + br + t   ___ ___ ough ___

6. + b + t   ___ ough ___

7. + f + t   ___ ough ___

voicesreading Grade 3

Copyright © Zaner-Bloser, Inc.

Name _____

Using an Index Answer the questions about the index below.

Index

allies, 25
Battle of Bull Run, 30
Civil War, 10, 22–30, 40, 52–55
Confederacy, 23
Grant, Ulysses S., 20
Lee, Robert E., 22
Lincoln, Abraham, 19, 22–24, 30–35
slavery, 23
Union, 24

1. What is page 20 about? _____

2. On which page can you read about Robert E. Lee?   _____

3. How many pages are under the heading Civil War?   _____

4. On which pages can you read about the Confederacy?   _____

5. Does this index show pages for cotton?   _____

6. Which topics can be found on page 23? _____

_____

7. Can you find information on Abraham Lincoln on page 20? _____

8. What type of book do you think this index is from? _____

_____

Name _____

More Multiple-Meaning Words (Homonyms) Read each pair of sentences. Write the homonym from the box that completes both sentences.

ring	fair	last	bill	story	toast

I. The _____ for my dentist appointment arrived today.

The duck's _____ is orange with white speckles.

2. Her _____ skin burns easily in the sun.

The county _____ lasts all week.

3. Are you the _____ person in line?

How long is this movie going to _____?

4. Mom gave me a _____ for my birthday.

Did you hear the telephone _____?

5. The main character in the _____ is a boy named Juan.

My aunt lives on the fourth _____ of the apartment building.

6. I like to eat _____ for breakfast.

The best man made a _____ to the bride and groom.

Name _____

Draw a line from the defintion to the vocabulary word in **dark print** that it matches.

l. peaceful   **occupations**

2. jobs
                                                        ensure

3. to make longer
                                                        violate

4. something
   beyond a
   basic need   **extend**

5. to go against;
   to defy   **nonviolent**

6. to make certain   **luxury**

Now, use each vocabulary word in a complete sentence.

7. _____

8. _____

9. _____

l0. _____

ll. _____

l2. _____

voicesreading Grade 3

Name _____

Cause and Effect Think about the story **¡Si, Se Puede! Yes, We Can!** Choose the effect from the box that completes each sentence. Write the words on the lines.

> his class painted signs
> she must work on the weekends
> they finally got the respect and pay raises
> the janitors decide to go on strike
> she can go to the park with Carlitos

1. Carlitos's mother cannot make enough money as a janitor, so

_____ .

2. It is not fair that the janitors work so hard, so _____

_____ .

3. Carlitos's class wanted to help with the strike, so _____

_____ .

4. The janitors let the building get dirtier and dirtier, so _____

_____ .

5. Carlitos's mother didn't have to work on the weekends

because she earned more money as a janitor. Now _____

_____ .

voicesreading Grade 3

Name _____

Comparing With Adverbs Circle the word or words that best complete each sentence.

I. I read (**slower, slowest**) than my brother does.

2. I listened (**more carefully, most carefully**) when I heard the information would be on the test.

3. I finished my chores (**more quickly, most quickly**) than Maria did.

4. Thomas sings (**louder, loudest**) than I do.

5. I swam the last lap (**faster, fastest**) than I swam the first three laps.

6. The car ran (**more smoothly, most smoothly**) after they changed the oil.

7. After I won the race, my sister cheered the (**louder, loudest**) of all.

8. Of all the dogs, Juma barks the (**louder, loudest**).

Theme 6: Freedom and Democracy **307**

Name _____

Action Plans Think about the speeches you have heard. Write down each student's name and what you liked about his or her speech. Then, you will vote on what you think the Action Plan should be.

Students' Names	Things I Liked About the Speech
I.	
2.	
3.	

I think our Action Plan should be _____

_____ .

voicesreading Grade 3

Name _____

Words With ough Write the word from the box that best completes each sentence.

dough	through	rough
cough	thought	tough

1. Mom and I walked _____ the park to get to the bus stop.

2. This sandpaper is _____ and scratchy.

3. I _____ yesterday was your birthday!

4. My throat hurts, and I have a _____.

5. The chef cooked the steak too long, so it's really

   _____ and hard to chew.

6. We make cookies with frozen cookie _____.

Name _____

Spelling Words

bought	brought	dough	fought
ought	though	thought	

Unscramble the letters in **dark print** to make spelling words from the box. Write the words correctly on the lines.

1. htougf _____

2. ghout _____

3. ghoutht _____

4. oughth _____

5. uboght _____

6. goduh _____

7. brghtou _____

Now, write a sentence with as many spelling words as you can.

_____

_____

_____

voicesreading Grade 3

Copyright © Zaner-Bloser, Inc.

Name _____

Dividing VCCCV Words Write the words from the box in **ABC order**. Draw a line between the syllables.

distract	conflict	instead	improve
subtract	complex	distrust	athlete
panther	lobster	sandwich	pumpkin

1. _____

2. _____

3. _____

4. _____

5. _____

6. _____

7. _____

8. _____

9. _____

10. _____

11. _____

12. _____

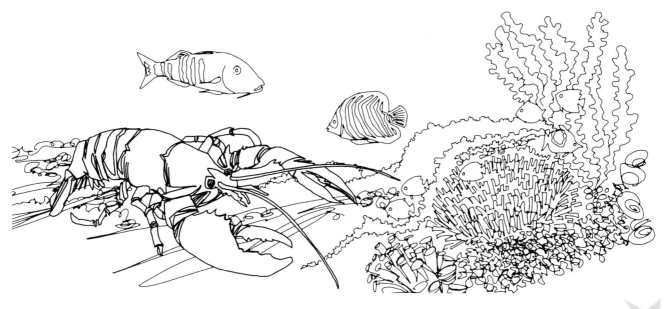

Name _____

Use the vocabulary words from the box to complete the paragraph.

outgoing	**ironic**	**zeal**
united	**ethnic**	**outspoken**

My friend Lupé has an _____ personality. She

makes new students feel comfortable when they come to our

class. It is _____ that her _____

to be friendly seems strange to some people. She is very

_____ in her belief that we should be nice to

each other. She feels this way because some students were not

friendly to her. When she was new to our school, some of us did

not understand her _____ background. She does

not want anyone else to have hurt feelings. Lupé taught me that

students should be _____ in kindness.

Name _____

Circle the vocabulary word that best completes each sentence.

I. Some _____ allow you to do exciting things such as jumping out of airplanes.

violations   **occupations**   **critics**   **keepsakes**

2. I was very happy when the teacher decided to _____ the deadline for our homework.

extend   **violate**   **prosper**   **contaminate**

3. Martin Luther King Jr. was a leader in the United States who believed in _____ ways of changing things.

luxurious   **contaminated**   **nonviolent**   **critic**

4. You must _____ that the gate is closed, or the goat will escape.

violate   **extend**   **isolate**   **ensure**

5. If you _____ the school rules, you will get in trouble.

prosper   **isolate**   **insist**   **violate**

6. A vacation to an exciting place is quite a _____.

luxury   **ensure**   **critic**   **refreshing**

Name _____

Noting Details Read the questions about the story **A River Ran Wild**. Write the answers on the lines.

I. What did the Native Americans give the white settlers in exchange for knives and beads?

_____

2. What kinds of animals lived near the river at first?

_____

3. Why did the Native Americans and the white settlers fight for one hundred years?

_____

_____

_____

4. Who did Oweana dream about one night?

_____

5. Why was Chief Weeawa crying in Oweana's dream?

_____

_____

6. How did the big industries pollute the river?

_____

voicesreading Grade 3

Name _____

Summarize Read the questions about the story **¡Si, Se Puede! Yes, We Can!** Write the answers on the lines.

1. What is the main idea of the story? _____

_____

2. What are 3 supporting details that support the main idea?

_____

_____

_____

_____

_____

3. Write a sentence or two using the information above to summarize the story.

_____

_____

_____

_____

Name _____

The Vowel + r Sound Write the word from the box that best completes each sentence. Write the word on the line.

stairs	chairs	parents	airplane
care	aware	square	share

I. Before the guests arrive, let's arrange the _____ around the table.

2. My family is flying in an _____ to South Dakota for vacation.

3. Are you _____ that your shirt is on backwards?

4. I _____ about dogs, so I volunteer at the animal shelter on Saturdays.

5. You have to climb many _____ to get to the third floor.

6. Amy's _____ pick her up from school every day.

7. Would you like to _____ this bag of pretzels with me?

8. A _____ is a shape with four equal sides.

Name _____

Draw a line from each vocabulary word in **dark print** to the definition it matches.

1. **foster**   an organization that has been set up with donated money

2. **thrived**

                                           to encourage

3. **acquire**

                                           experienced sadness

4. **grieved**

                                           to get; to collect

5. **foundation**   admitted as a member

6. **inducted**   grew; did well

Name _____

Words With ough Circle the word that best completes each sentence.

I. We drive _____ three long tunnels on our way to Grandma's house.

   though   **thought**   **through**   **threw**

2. I _____ the school play was better this year than it's ever been.

   thought   **tough**   **though**   **through**

3. The spelling test was really _____, but I think I did well.

   though   **thought**   **trough**   **tough**

4. Even _____ my brother is silly sometimes, I still love him.

   thought   **though**   **through**   **tough**

5. The farmer dumped food scraps into a large _____ for the pigs.

   tough   **through**   **trough**   **thought**

6. My room needs a _____ cleaning before I can play.

   thorough   **through**   **trough**   **throughout**

7. It snowed _____ the day, so we might not have school tomorrow.

   thought   **thorough**   **throughout**   **trough**

8. My cat's tongue feels _____, like sandpaper, when she licks me.

   cough   **rough**   **ought**   **taught**

Name _____

Spelling Words

| air | airplane | care | dare | éclair | fair |
| fairy tale | flare | glare | hair | pair | share |

Circle the hidden spelling words.

```
G  L  A  I  R  P  L  A  N  E
L  S  H  A  R  E  A  I  E  C
A  I  A  L  A  R  E  L  N  L
R  A  I  K  D  D  A  R  E  A
E  U  R  A  X  T  P  U  G  I
C  A  N  I  Y  U  P  G  E  R
T  R  E  R  U  F  A  I  R  O
O  U  I  H  O  W  I  C  A  V
C  A  R  E  O  P  R  D  Q  L
F  L  A  R  E  S  Z  W  U  D
```

Name _____

More Irregular Verbs Circle the verb that best completes each sentence.

1. I rushed down the hall when I heard the tardy bell ring.

   The bell (**ringed, rang**) three times.

2. My brother is going to bring my lunch to school.

   I should have (**brought, brings**) it with me.

3. My sister sings in the school choir.

   She (**sang, singed**) in the play last year.

4. I would like to give my parents a special gift this year.

   I (**given, gave**) them books last year.

5. I will take the bus to school next year.

   Only the older students (**took, take**) the bus last year.

6. I eat fruit with cereal every morning for breakfast.

   I (**ate, eaten**) a banana this morning.

7. I sleep in a bunk bed that I share with my cousin.

   I (**slept, sleeped**) at my friend's house last weekend.

8. Let's go to the park today.

   We (**gone, went**) to the pumpkin patch yesterday.

voicesreading Grade 3

Copyright © Zaner-Bloser, Inc.

Name _____

Writing a Thank-You Letter to My Teacher Think about how your teacher has helped you this year. Write your ideas below. Express your thoughts clearly. Then give your letter to your teacher.

Dear _____ ,

_____

_____

_____

_____

_____

_____

_____

_____

_____ ,

_____

voicesreading Grade 3

Name _____

The Vowel + r Sound Read the words in each tic-tac-toe board. Draw a line through the three words in each board that have the same vowel sound.

voicesreading Grade 3

I.

fair	far	hair
car	dare	star
stare	care	pain

2.

fair	fear	bear
scar	war	pair
pear	war	care

3.

rare	cart	bar
tart	air	blare
start	dear	bare

4.

sail	part	jail
flare	fair	wear
paint	stair	tail

Copyright © Zaner-Bloser, Inc.

Name _____

Spelling Words

air	airplane	care	dare	éclair	fair
fairy tale	flare	glare	hair	pair	share

Unscramble the letters in **dark print** to make spelling words from the box. Write the words correctly on the lines.

1. **panelria** _____

2. **clairé** _____

3. **ahir** _____

4. **arec** _____

5. **ipar** _____

6. **hares** _____

7. **airf** _____

8. **rade** _____

9. **tairy fale** _____

10. **laref** _____

11. **large** _____

12. **ria** _____

Name _____

Proofread each sentence. Circle the misspelled word. Write the spelling word correctly on the line.

I. My favorite faree tail is about a dragon that learns to square dance.

_____

2. The aire is smoky because a dragon tried to burn down the dance hall.

_____

3. Would you like to shair this piece of pie with me?

_____

4. No, thank you. I am eating this yummy éclare.

_____

5. The airplain flew toward San Francisco. _____

6. She put on her sunglasses because there was a glair from the sun.

_____

7. The clown bought a pare of very large shoes.

_____

8. Her hare is in a braid.

_____

9. "I dair you to walk through the dark forest," he said.

_____

10. The frightened hiker fired a flair into the sky.

_____

II. Rebecca took good cair of the lost kitten.

_____

12. The pig won a blue ribbon at the county fare.

_____

voicesreading Grade 3

Name _____

Write the vocabulary word from the box that best completes each sentence.

thrived	**foster**	**grieved**
acquire	**inducted**	**foundation**

1. Our teacher told us that being active will _____ good health.

2. The wealthy woman started a _____ to help needy children.

3. My parents decided to _____ a car that would use less fuel.

4. I'm happy they _____ my favorite player into the Hall of Fame.

5. The plant _____ when we put it in the sunny window.

6. The boy _____ when his dog ran away.

My Handbook

This handbook is designed for writers like you! It contains some graphic organizers that you can use for your thoughts and ideas. You can use this handbook any time you need extra help with your writing.

Table of Contents

You can use a **Web** to organize your ideas for writing.

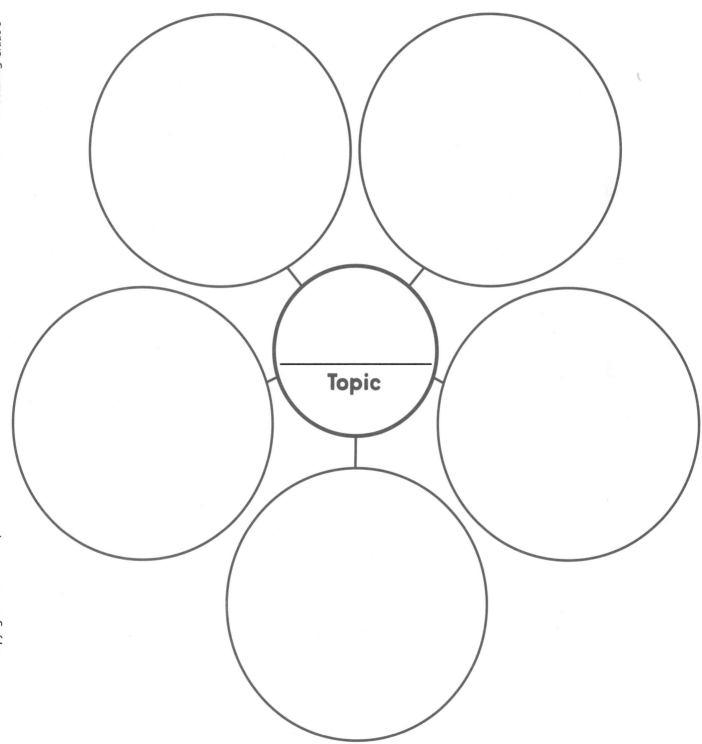

Topic

Story Map

A **Story Map** helps you organize your ideas about people and places in narrative writing.

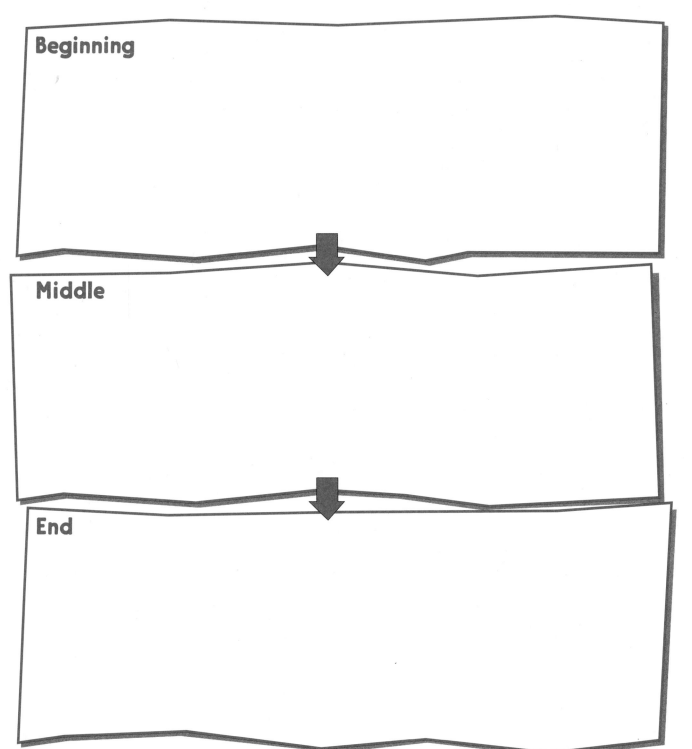

Beginning

Middle

End

voicesreading Grade 3

Expository writing is easier when you use a **Spider Map** to organize details.

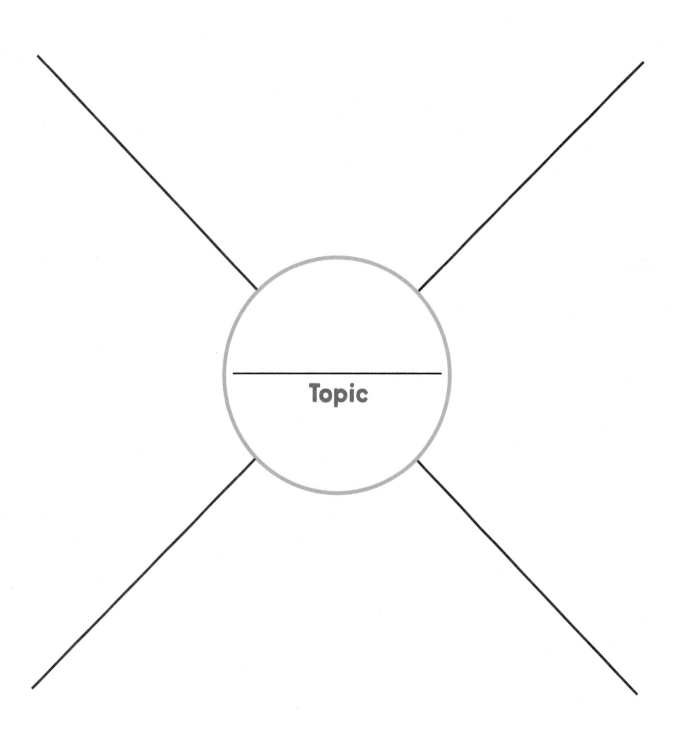

Topic

Character Trait Chart

You can use a **Character Trait Chart** to organize your ideas about characters in your stories.

voicesreading Grade 3

Character:

What He or She Looks Like	How He or She Acts

Character:

What He or She Looks Like	How He or She Acts

An **Attribute Chart** makes comparing two things easier.

_____	**Attribute**	_____

Problem-Solution Frame

Figuring out the problems and solutions to a conflict is easier when you use a **Problem-Solution Frame**.

Problem Box

What is the problem?

Why is it a problem?

Who has the problem?

Solution Box

Solutions

Results

End Result Box

You can use a **Timeline** to organize events for your writing.

Events

Dates

A **Persuasion Map** can help you organize your ideas for persuasive writing.

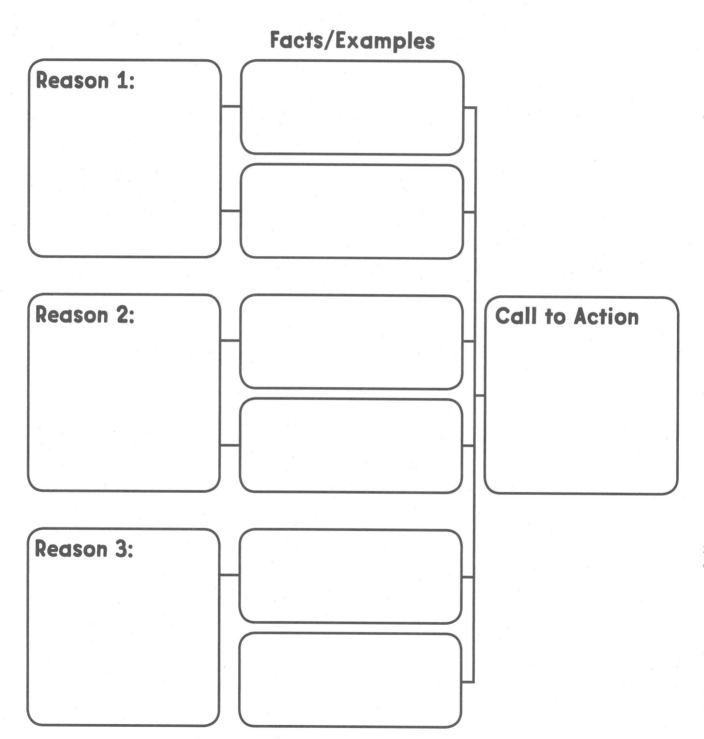

Facts/Examples

Reason 1:

Reason 2:

Call to Action

Reason 3:

Order-of-Importance Chart

Organizing your reasons for persuasive writing is easier when you use an **Order-of-Importance Chart**.

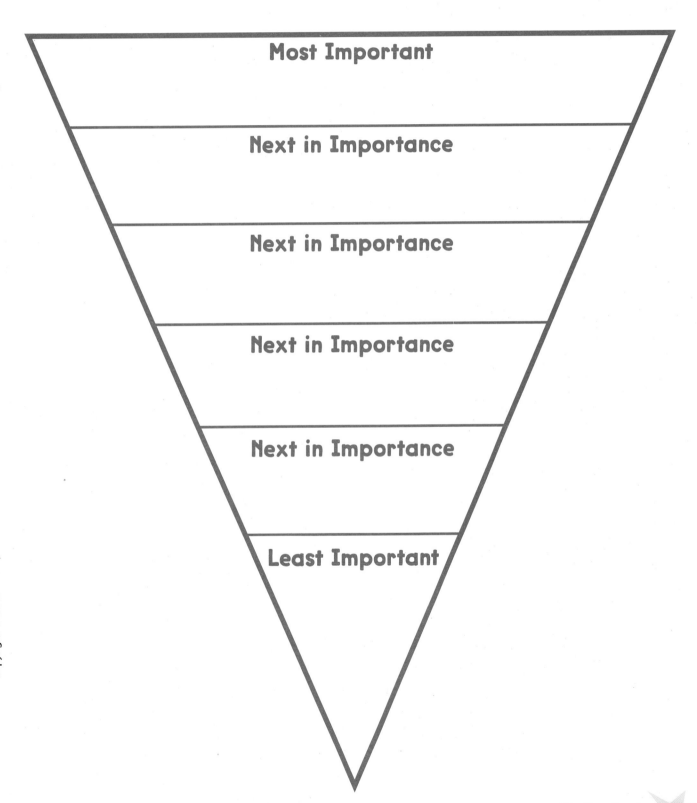

Most Important

Next in Importance

Next in Importance

Next in Importance

Next in Importance

Least Important

Main Idea Table

You can use a **Main Idea Table** to organize ideas for your writing.

Main Idea:

Supporting Detail:

Supporting Detail:

Supporting Detail:

Supporting Detail:

High-Frequency Word Cards Theme 4, Week 3	**High-Frequency Word Cards** Theme 4, Week 2	**High-Frequency Word Cards** Theme 4, Week 1
captain	suppose	control
caught	received	equal
desert	visit	party
direct	whose	practice
strange	woman	straight

voicesreading

Grade 3, Theme 4, Week 1

© Zaner-Bloser, Inc.

voicesreading

Grade 3, Theme 4, Week 2

© Zaner-Bloser, Inc.

voicesreading

Grade 3, Theme 4, Week 3

© Zaner-Bloser, Inc.

voicesreading

Grade 3, Theme 4, Week 1

© Zaner-Bloser, Inc.

voicesreading

Grade 3, Theme 4, Week 2

© Zaner-Bloser, Inc.

voicesreading

Grade 3, Theme 4, Week 3

© Zaner-Bloser, Inc.

voicesreading

Grade 3, Theme 4, Week 1

© Zaner-Bloser, Inc.

voicesreading

Grade 3, Theme 4, Week 2

© Zaner-Bloser, Inc.

voicesreading

Grade 3, Theme 4, Week 3

© Zaner-Bloser, Inc.

voicesreading

Grade 3, Theme 4, Week 1

© Zaner-Bloser, Inc.

voicesreading

Grade 3, Theme 4, Week 2

© Zaner-Bloser, Inc.

voicesreading

Grade 3, Theme 4, Week 3

© Zaner-Bloser, Inc.

voicesreading

Grade 3, Theme 4, Week 1

© Zaner-Bloser, Inc.

voicesreading

Grade 3, Theme 4, Week 2

© Zaner-Bloser, Inc.

voicesreading

Grade 3, Theme 4, Week 3

© Zaner-Bloser, Inc.

voicesreading

Grade 3, Theme 4, Week 1

© Zaner-Bloser, Inc.

voicesreading

Grade 3, Theme 4, Week 2

© Zaner-Bloser, Inc.

voicesreading

Grade 3, Theme 4, Week 3

© Zaner-Bloser, Inc.

board	doctor	break
compound	human	business
modern	insects	history
provide	lady	separate
won't	supply	uncle

voicesreading

Grade 3, Theme 4, Week 4

© Zaner-Bloser, Inc.

voicesreading

Grade 3, Theme 4, Week 5

© Zaner-Bloser, Inc.

voicesreading

Grade 3, Theme 4, Week 6

© Zaner-Bloser, Inc.

voicesreading

Grade 3, Theme 4, Week 4

© Zaner-Bloser, Inc.

voicesreading

Grade 3, Theme 4, Week 5

© Zaner-Bloser, Inc.

voicesreading

Grade 3, Theme 4, Week 6

© Zaner-Bloser, Inc.

voicesreading

Grade 3, Theme 4, Week 4

© Zaner-Bloser, Inc.

voicesreading

Grade 3, Theme 4, Week 5

© Zaner-Bloser, Inc.

voicesreading

Grade 3, Theme 4, Week 6

© Zaner-Bloser, Inc.

voicesreading

Grade 3, Theme 4, Week 4

© Zaner-Bloser, Inc.

voicesreading

Grade 3, Theme 4, Week 5

© Zaner-Bloser, Inc.

voicesreading

Grade 3, Theme 4, Week 6

© Zaner-Bloser, Inc.

voicesreading

Grade 3, Theme 4, Week 4

© Zaner-Bloser, Inc.

voicesreading

Grade 3, Theme 4, Week 5

© Zaner-Bloser, Inc.

voicesreading

Grade 3, Theme 4, Week 6

© Zaner-Bloser, Inc.

voicesreading

Grade 3, Theme 4, Week 4

© Zaner-Bloser, Inc.

voicesreading

Grade 3, Theme 4, Week 5

© Zaner-Bloser, Inc.

voicesreading

Grade 3, Theme 4, Week 6

© Zaner-Bloser, Inc.

High-Frequency Word Cards	High-Frequency Word Cards	High-Frequency Word Cards
Theme 5, Week 3	Theme 5, Week 2	Theme 5, Week 1
famous	crowd	addition
interesting	except	compare
lie	expect	guess
movement	indicate	soldiers
value	poem	wasn't

voicesreading

Grade 3, Theme 5, Week 1

© Zaner-Bloser, Inc.

voicesreading

Grade 3, Theme 5, Week 2

© Zaner-Bloser, Inc.

voicesreading

Grade 3, Theme 5, Week 3

© Zaner-Bloser, Inc.

voicesreading

Grade 3, Theme 5, Week 1

© Zaner-Bloser, Inc.

voicesreading

Grade 3, Theme 5, Week 2

© Zaner-Bloser, Inc.

voicesreading

Grade 3, Theme 5, Week 3

© Zaner-Bloser, Inc.

voicesreading

Grade 3, Theme 5, Week 1

© Zaner-Bloser, Inc.

voicesreading

Grade 3, Theme 5, Week 2

© Zaner-Bloser, Inc.

voicesreading

Grade 3, Theme 5, Week 3

© Zaner-Bloser, Inc.

voicesreading

Grade 3, Theme 5, Week 1

© Zaner-Bloser, Inc.

voicesreading

Grade 3, Theme 5, Week 2

© Zaner-Bloser, Inc.

voicesreading

Grade 3, Theme 5, Week 3

© Zaner-Bloser, Inc.

voicesreading

Grade 3, Theme 5, Week 1

© Zaner-Bloser, Inc.

voicesreading

Grade 3, Theme 5, Week 2

© Zaner-Bloser, Inc.

voicesreading

Grade 3, Theme 5, Week 3

© Zaner-Bloser, Inc.

voicesreading

Grade 3, Theme 5, Week 1

© Zaner-Bloser, Inc.

voicesreading

Grade 3, Theme 5, Week 2

© Zaner-Bloser, Inc.

voicesreading

Grade 3, Theme 5, Week 3

© Zaner-Bloser, Inc.

High-Frequency Word Cards	High-Frequency Word Cards	High-Frequency Word Cards
Theme 5, Week 6	Theme 5, Week 5	Theme 5, Week 4
major	chief	consider
necessary	dollars	entered
observe	planets	position
science	rhythm	suggested
weight	sight	tied

voicesreading

Grade 3, Theme 5, Week 4

voicesreading

Grade 3, Theme 5, Week 5

voicesreading

Grade 3, Theme 5, Week 6

voicesreading

Grade 3, Theme 5, Week 4

voicesreading

Grade 3, Theme 5, Week 5

voicesreading

Grade 3, Theme 5, Week 6

voicesreading

Grade 3, Theme 5, Week 4

voicesreading

Grade 3, Theme 5, Week 5

voicesreading

Grade 3, Theme 5, Week 6

voicesreading

Grade 3, Theme 5, Week 4

voicesreading

Grade 3, Theme 5, Week 5

voicesreading

Grade 3, Theme 5, Week 6

voicesreading

Grade 3, Theme 5, Week 4

voicesreading

Grade 3, Theme 5, Week 5

voicesreading

Grade 3, Theme 5, Week 6

voicesreading

Grade 3, Theme 5, Week 4

voicesreading

Grade 3, Theme 5, Week 5

voicesreading

Grade 3, Theme 5, Week 6

High-Frequency Word Cards

Theme 6, Week 3

High-Frequency Word Cards

Theme 6, Week 2

High-Frequency Word Cards

Theme 6, Week 1

ahead	spread	current
column	action	industry
level	company	process
southern	factories	property
wouldn't	radio	shoulder

© Zaner-Bloser, Inc.

voicesreading

Grade 3, Theme 6, Week 1

© Zaner-Bloser, Inc.

voicesreading

Grade 3, Theme 6, Week 2

© Zaner-Bloser, Inc.

voicesreading

Grade 3, Theme 6, Week 3

© Zaner-Bloser, Inc.

voicesreading

Grade 3, Theme 6, Week 1

© Zaner-Bloser, Inc.

voicesreading

Grade 3, Theme 6, Week 2

© Zaner-Bloser, Inc.

voicesreading

Grade 3, Theme 6, Week 3

© Zaner-Bloser, Inc.

voicesreading

Grade 3, Theme 6, Week 1

© Zaner-Bloser, Inc.

voicesreading

Grade 3, Theme 6, Week 2

© Zaner-Bloser, Inc.

voicesreading

Grade 3, Theme 6, Week 3

© Zaner-Bloser, Inc.

voicesreading

Grade 3, Theme 6, Week 1

© Zaner-Bloser, Inc.

voicesreading

Grade 3, Theme 6, Week 2

© Zaner-Bloser, Inc.

voicesreading

Grade 3, Theme 6, Week 3

© Zaner-Bloser, Inc.

voicesreading

Grade 3, Theme 6, Week 1

© Zaner-Bloser, Inc.

voicesreading

Grade 3, Theme 6, Week 2

© Zaner-Bloser, Inc.

voicesreading

Grade 3, Theme 6, Week 3

© Zaner-Bloser, Inc.

voicesreading

Grade 3, Theme 6, Week 1

© Zaner-Bloser, Inc.

voicesreading

Grade 3, Theme 6, Week 2

© Zaner-Bloser, Inc.

voicesreading

Grade 3, Theme 6, Week 3

© Zaner-Bloser, Inc.

adjective	afraid	opposite
forward	especially	oxygen
office	prepared	plural
similar	solution	various
sugar	wrong	western

voicesreading

Grade 3, Theme 6, Week 4

voicesreading

Grade 3, Theme 6, Week 5

voicesreading

Grade 3, Theme 6, Week 6

voicesreading

Grade 3, Theme 6, Week 4

voicesreading

Grade 3, Theme 6, Week 5

voicesreading

Grade 3, Theme 6, Week 6

voicesreading

Grade 3, Theme 6, Week 4

voicesreading

Grade 3, Theme 6, Week 5

voicesreading

Grade 3, Theme 6, Week 6

voicesreading

Grade 3, Theme 6, Week 4

voicesreading

Grade 3, Theme 6, Week 5

voicesreading

Grade 3, Theme 6, Week 6

voicesreading

Grade 3, Theme 6, Week 4

voicesreading

Grade 3, Theme 6, Week 5

voicesreading

Grade 3, Theme 6, Week 6

voicesreading

Grade 3, Theme 6, Week 4

voicesreading

Grade 3, Theme 6, Week 5

voicesreading

Grade 3, Theme 6, Week 6